Review copy only

Not for sale

Great Masters of Beekeeping

Old English Black Bee. A much enlarged picture from Samuel Bagster's 'The Management of Bees' (1834): Queen, Worker and (bottom) Drone. Drawn by Charles Curtis in 1833 and engraved by D. Dodd in 1834.

GREAT MASTERS OF BEEKEEPING

RON BROWN

BEE BOOKS NEW & OLD
TAPPING WALL FARM, BURROWBRIDGE
SOMERSET

ISBN 0 905652 31 2

By the same author:

One Thousand Years of Devon Beekeeping, 1975, Devon Beekeepers' Assn, Newton Abbot

Beekeeping: A Seasonal Guide, 1985, B T Batsford Ltd, London (3rd printing, 1992)

Honey Bees: A Guide to Management, 1988, The Crowood Press, Marlborough (2nd edition, 1990)

Beeswax, 1981, Bee Books New & Old, Burrowbridge (2nd edition, 1989)

All Round the Compass, 1993, Janus Publishing, London

Filmset in Ehrhardt by Selwood Systems, Midsomer Norton

Printed in Great Britain by Butler & Tanner Ltd, Frome and London

CONTENTS

ILLUSTRATIONS

ACKNOWLEDGEMENTS

It is difficult to pay adequate tribute to, or even acknowledge all those who have helped and encouraged me in researching and writing this book; if I mention but a few (and probably omit many) please forgive me, as sources have been so rich and varied. From the great 17th century diarists Pepys and Evelyn to files of local newspapers on microfilm. From the British Museum to the archives of Reading University. From the library of IBRA in Cardiff to the Cowan Library in the Ministry of Agriculture, Whitehall. The yearly bound early editions of the 'British Bee Journal' from its beginning in 1873 have been in constant use in my home library: in the absence of specialist bee journals before this, the great beekeepers wrote in 'The Times' and several periodicals, but most richly in the journals of The Royal Horticultural Society, founded in 1804, to which I have been granted ready access in London. In many cases books written by the Great Masters themselves have helped enormously, from Rev. Charles Butler's 'Feminine Monarchie' of 1609 to Rev. Bro. Adam's 'Bee-keeping at Buckfast Abbey' of 1975. Some of the more recent masters I have had the privilege of knowing personally over the past 50 years and have been able to use communications directly from them. In other cases the careers of beekeepers centuries ago have involved following up clues in most unlikely places, such as the Methodist Library in Gordon Square, London (for Rev. Jacob Isaac), or the records of Trinity College, Cambridge (for one-time Master, Bishop John Wilkin). I have greatly enjoyed working on this project, which has occupied much of my spare time over the last three years.

I wish to express my sincere appreciation of Karl Showler's work in so kindly checking the proofs of this text. I also thank Peter Rosenfelt, Editor of 'Beekeeping', for his constant encouragement, as well as for publishing many of these biographical studies over the past three years. I am grateful to Ron Wood of Newbury for his kindness and skill in taking colour photographs of the stained glass window in Charles Butler's old church at Wootton St. Lawrence, for the cover of this book. I also acknowledge the invaluable help of Anita Stokes, who has typed every page of this book at least once, as I have altered, added to or deleted successive drafts.

Torquay
November 1993

Ron Brown

CHAPTER ONE

THE REV. DR CHARLES BUTLER 1559–1647

Born at High Wycombe, Bucks, entered Magdalene Hall, Oxford in 1579; graduated B.A. 1583, M.A. 1587; stayed on at University as bible clerk and chorister until 1593. Then after 2 years as rector of Nately, he served from 1595–1600 as Master of the Holy Ghost School, Basingstoke, and from then until his death as Vicar of Wootton St Lawrence (near Basingstoke). He was a great scholar and musician, Doctor of Divinity, author of musical works including 'Principles of Music', 'Oratoria' as well as his great book 'Feminine Monarchie' published in 1609 (revised edition 1623). He also formulated a system of phonetic spelling.

Throughout his long life Butler kept bees in straw skeps bound with split brambles, but also described the old wicker hives made like baskets with willow or hazel twigs; both were 'cloomed' i.e. daubed with cowdung mixed with either ashes or lime plus a little sand or very fine gravel. His normal hive measured 17 inches from top to bottom with a capacity of 3 pecks (6 gallons—just under 1 cubic foot), roughly equivalent to 9 National frames.

For larger swarms he preferred a bushel hive (8 gallons—about $1\frac{1}{3}$ cubic feet), slightly larger than an 11 frame National, but of course with no supers. His management system was based on swarming, collecting and hiving his own (and no doubt others) in May, June and early July. An accurate observer and recorder, he speaks of a 'good swarm' as weighing about 5 pounds with some 'very good' a pound heavier, but many others weighing only $2\frac{1}{2}$–4 pounds. He says that bees in a swarm weigh in at 4480 to the pound.

He gives clear directions for management throughout the year, and normally harvested his honey in August by driving the bees up into an empty skep and then running them back after cutting out the honey; he then fed them with some honey. He never killed bees over a sulphur pit as so many beekeepers did in those days.

Apiary Sites

Butler preferred a site protected to the North by a house, tall wall or very thick hedge, with quickset hedge on the other three sides to give some shelter, especially for bees landing with heavy loads and fatigued. Long grass and weeds around the hive were to be avoided, as they made it more difficult for the bees to fly up, and also harboured enemies. He pointed out how homing bees flew close to the ground and in the lee of hedges when it was windy. A bee garden should also have trees and bushes fit to receive swarms; plum, cherry, apple, hazel and filbert, for example, with convenient boughs not too high.

His skeps were kept on individual stools 2 feet apart, each with a slight forward slope so that rain might not run into the hive, nor stay at the door. Stool legs were 12–13 inches long to enable them to be pushed 3–4 inches into the ground and still carry the hives about 9 inches up. The tops of the stools were made one inch wider than the hives on three sides, but three inches wider in front to give space for the bees to alight. The hives were placed in rows running E–W, with entrances facing SSW. His ideal apiary measured at least 50 feet square for 7 ranks of 5.

Hives

Each straw hive (or skep) was fitted with a thick 'Coppe' or circular piece of wood inside at the top. The upper surface rounded to fit into and support the domed top, the lower surface flat but with a half-inch deep hole in the centre. This was to take 3 or 4 'Spleets', pliable split hazel or willow sticks, pushed in from the base and bowed to lodge in the straw about an inch or two up. Of such a length as to lie back to back, these served to support the combs when built and also help maintain the shape of the skep. All hives were fitted with 'Hackles' made of wheat or rye straw bound tightly at the top and splayed out into a cone. In winter these were belted round the middle of hives, but removed occasionally on mild and windy days to shake out moths, spiders and earwigs, check for mouse damage and air the hives after much wet weather. As already mentioned, all hives were cloomed with cowdung and ashes, which was said to be a good protection against the gnawing of mice. Doors or entrances were cut into the base of each hive, with arrangements for narrowing to provide 4 square inches for bees in high summer, but very much reduced for the rest of the year.

Bees

Butler described the queen as about 1 inch long, more than a worker by about a third. Her back was of brighter brown than the workers, and her belly was described as a 'sad yellow', deeper than the richest gold, in other words a coppery gold in colour. Her legs were longer and more amber than those of a worker. Her wings were about the same size as those of a simple bee, so that they seem short on her, more like a cloak than a gown. Where the workers had three whitish or lighter rings, the queen had a golden bar.

Drones were described as being 'grosse hive-bees without stings, quick to feed slow to work, for howsoever they brave it with their round velvet caps, full paunches and load roar, yet they are but idle companions, living by the sweat of others' brows'. Yet the function of drones was recognized—in his own words, 'for albeit he be not seene to engender with the honey-bee, either abroad as other insects doe, or within the hive, yet without doubt he is the male-bee, by whose masculine virtue bees are secretly conceived and bred.' He also spoke of two testes noted in the anatomy of a drone, and mentioned that Dorres (bumble bees) had drones 'which did openly engender with their females'. The role of drones in helping to keep the brood warm by their body heat was also described, as was throwing out the drones in late summer. He also observed that the hives which got rid of their drones first were likely to be the best hives in the following summer.

Swarms and Swarming

Butler said that most hives swarmed between 9 May–11 July, but in some backward years like 1621 and 1622 when the bramble was

2–3 weeks late in flowering, there were swarms between 12 July–12 August. Throughout the book he uses the signs of the zodiac instead of calendar months. (See Appendix p. 17)

He was well-informed about swarms, and said firmly that swarms had bees of all ages, not just young bees. He also made the point that 'if any man desire to see the queen, he hath now opportunity, when she goes forth with the swarm. Swarms normally come forth between 9 and 3, chiefly between 11 and 1 o'clock; generally they prefer the forenoon.' 'A wet summer gives two causes for swarming, plenty of bees and not much honey; the one maketh them able, the other willing, and then neither wind nor cloud nor rain can stay them.' The year 1616 was apparently an extraordinary year of plenty, both for honey and for swarms, in effect as good as two summers in one.

He clearly described 'scout-bees' or 'spies' which dance and shake their wings on a clustered swarm, persuading others to do the same. He advises 'When this "shivering" spreads to bees all round the cluster, then you may bid them farewell. So, as soon as a swarm has settled, hive them.' This comes very close to the discovery by Karl von Frisch over 300 years later, and suggests that Butler may have had an idea that the 'scout-bees' directed the others; however he failed to link this behaviour and the subsequent departure of the swarm, with the 'spies' guiding the swarm to a selected place, in so many words.

On the actual taking and hiving of a swarm he says, 'The manner of hiving is so manifold, by reason of the many and different circumstances, that it can hardly be taught by precept but has to be learned by use and experience, guided with reason and discretion.' However he goes on to describe common situations such as shaking, cutting off a bough, brushing bees off a tree-trunk or driving them up a thick hedge into a skep placed on top.

He also specifies swarm-catching equipment like a brush and a sheet at least 3 feet square but preferably larger. For driving he recommends burning a little hay, to give plenty of smoke but no flame, and comments that bees may be driven by smoke out of a hollow tree or chimney only on the day they arrive or the day after. How true!

After 'Cancer is well entered' (July) he liked to run 2 or 3 swarms together, whether they had risen all on the same day or over several days, and normally he had no trouble in so doing.

However, he records that on 26 June 1621 he had two fair swarms up at once, which put together over-filled a good hive, and then fought from Thursday noon to Saturday, both queens and half the hive dying. Those left rose out of the hive and peacefully joined up with a hive behind them, where they were quietly received. This was quoted as a most unusual happening, rather than as a danger to be expected. An example of 'bees never doing anything invariably' as another well-known beekeeper was to say two and a half centuries later.

The Seasons of the Year
SPRING (February, March April) 'The sunne with quickning heat, beginneth to revive the flowers. The bees having tasted thereof, begin to breed and increase their numbers for the coming summer.'
SUMMER (May, June, July) 'At the coming of the swallow, the time is most rich and plentiful in flowers and dews, wherewith the multiplied bees do now store their cells against the poverty of winter.' Also 'When a dry summer follows a wet spring, the harvest is rich.'
AUTUMN (August, September, October) 'In which the bee-masters, and the master-bees, do reap the ripe fruit of many bees' labours.'
WINTER (November, December, January) 'In which the bees live altogether upon their summer stores, and get nothing.'

Butler speaks of August as the most dangerous time for bees, because of the wasps which then, if not sooner, learn their way into the hives. As also do robbing bees. He advised very narrow entrances at this time, except for very strong hives which are safe enough. He says that wasps and robber bees will be stealing early in the morning, before the true bees are stirring, and advises closing up entrances of weak hives until 10 or 11 o'clock.

Nectar Sources (near Basingstoke, Hants)
Among the very first he lists Winter Gilifloure, the Dazy and

the herb Bearefoot (Hellebore). Then Box, Withy-palme (Pussy Willow), Daffadill, Lide-Lilie, Blackthorne. In Taurus, Plum-tree, Dandelion, Gooseberry, Cherry, Peare, Bluebell. Followed by Apple, Crab, Rosemary, Beech, Vetch and Maple. In Gemini, as well as Vetch and Maple in their prime come Beanes, Arch-angell (Dead Nettle), Barberie, Fumitorie, Ribworte, Hollie, Hawthorne, Red Honie-suckle, White Honie-suckle (which they like much better than the red). In Cancer, the Three-leafed Grasse, Benet, Malowes, Tyme (yieldeth most and best honie). Then Knapweed and Blackberie a week after. 'Now the greatest plenty of Nectar cometh from above, distilled out of the air from flowers and received on oak and other forest trees, on their leaves as honeydew. The hotter and drier the Summer is, the greater and more frequent are the Honie-dewes, drawn up into the air from flowers by the hot sun and condensing on leaves during the cool nights. In Virgo and Libra comes honie from the Heath and the Ivy, and Scorpio from the Ivy.'

Water

'Bees have most need of water in the cold, windie weather of Spring, when many are so chilled when they have filled themselves with cold water that they are drowned, or fail and fall by the way.' Butler designed a shallow wooden trough for his bees, with a wooden float that could rise and fall with the water.

He placed this a perch away from his hives (5–6 yards).

Advice to Beekeepers

'If thou wilt have the favour of thy Bees that they sting ye not, thou must not come among them smelling of sweat or having a stinking breath caused by eating of Onions, Garleeke and the like. Thou must not be given to surfeiting and drunkenness: thou must not come puffing and blowing, neither hastily stirre among them, nor violently defend thy selfe when they seem to threaten thee, but softly moving thy hand before thy face, gently put them by. Lastly thou must be no stranger unto them. In a word thou must be chaste, cleanly, sweet, sober, quiet and familiar: so will they love thee, and know thee from all others.'

APPENDIX

The Zodiacal Months, corrected for the '11 days'

Aries	10 Mar–9 Apr
Taurus	10 Apr–10 May
Gemini	11 May–10 Jun
Cancer	11 Jun–11 Jul
Leo	12 Jul–12 Aug
Virgo	13 Aug–12 Sep
Libra	13 Sep–12 Oct
Scorpio	13 Oct–11 Nov
Sagittarius	12 Nov–10 Dec
Capricorn	11 Dec–9 Jan
Aquarius	10 Jan–8 Feb
Pisces	9 Feb–9 Mar

CHAPTER TWO

THE RIGHT REV. DR JOHN WILKINS F.R.S. 1614–1672

Wilkins was one of the great beekeepers of the 17th century, who kept bees in Exeter when he held the office of Prebendary at the Cathedral and elsewhere as his career progressed via Oxford, Cambridge, St Paul's and finally to a Bishopric in historic Chester.

From 1648 to 1659 he was Warden of Wadham College, Oxford, where he kept bees in the garden of the Warden's Lodge. He was active in the Philosophic Society, which took great interest in all things scientific, from thunderstorms to magnetism, in astronomy and above all—bees. A kindred spirit was young Christopher Wren, a student at the University, and this association continued when the two were both in London, and were foremost in the formation of the Royal Society, of which Wilkins was the first Secretary, with premises at Gresham's College.

From Oxford, Wilkins proceeded to Cambridge in 1659, having been appointed Master of Trinity College. However within a year he left for London where he was greatly concerned with the formation in 1660 of the Philosophic Society, which two years later was given the Royal Charter by Charles II: John Evelyn's diary records several meetings with Wilkins at the Royal Society: King Charles also attended such meetings regularly, and obviously would have known Wilkins—hence presumably his preferment to the Bishopric of Chester. Apart from a keen general interest in science, these three were all concerned with bees. In a diary entry for 24 November 1661 Evelyn wrote: 'This night his Majestie fell into discourse with me concerning bees.' Those who read this book will understand—but just what was discussed we shall never know. Over 300 years later the most prized award in science is still the Fellowship of the Royal Society, and the proud letters, 'F.R.S.' Our own Colin Butler received this award for his great work on queen substance and related pheromones in the '50s and '60s, almost exactly 300 years after Robert Hooke presented the first microscopic study of a bee sting with detailed drawings, and duly became an 'F.R.S.'

John Wilkins and his beekeeping are described by John Evelyn, the great diarist, as follows:
'10 July 1654—supp'd at a magnificent entertainment in Wadham Hall, with my dear friend Dr. Wilkins the Warden.
11 July—met that miracle of a youth Mr. Christopher Wren, nephew to ye Bishop of Ely.
13 July—we all din'd at that most obliging and universally curious Dr. Wilkins', at Wadham College, who shewed me his transparent hives, so order'd one upon another as to take the honey without destroying the bees. He was so abundantly civil, as finding me pleased with them, to present me with one of ye hives which he had empty, and wch I afterwards had in my garden at Sayes Court, where it continu'd for many years, and

which his majestie came on purpose to see and contemplate with much satisfaction.'

Another great diarist (Pepys) commented on the fascination of this hive, which he too saw and admired in Evelyn's garden.

In fact King Charles had copies of this hive made for himself in his own apiary, managed by Moses Rusden, the King's Beemaster.

In his 'Natural History of Oxfordshire' 1677, Dr Robert. Plot referred to the 'new sort of bee boxes' set up in Wadham College garden by Bishop Wilkins in 1652 and still there when he wrote. He derided John Gedde's claim to have invented them in 1668 and to have used them for the last seven years.

Historically-minded readers may wonder how the career of this talented beekeeper progressed so steadily through such troublesome times, covering the beheading of King Charles I, the Protectorate of Oliver Cromwell and finally the restoration of the Monarchy in the person of King Charles II. His marriage to Oliver's sister Robina might explain his advancement during the Protectorate, yet in 1668 the monarch approved his appointment as Bishop of Chester, where he died in office 'of the stone' only four years later. We know that Charles II was interested in science and in beekeeping; the mode and timing of Wilkins' death suggest that he was a 'bon viveur', another characteristic shared with his king.

What has this to do with modern beekeeping? Well, the hive of 1652 was the first to be constructed of several identical boxes, one upon another. This is universal practice now in all the major beekeeping countries, using only Langstroth deep boxes, with complete standardization. Secondly, some of the keenest minds of the period, led by John Wilkins and his young friend Christopher Wren, were laying the foundations of modern beekeeping, of using supers and not killing the bees to take their honey. If only they had appreciated the significance of the bee space and achieved movable frames as a consequence, the world would not have had to wait another 200 years for L. L. Langstroth.

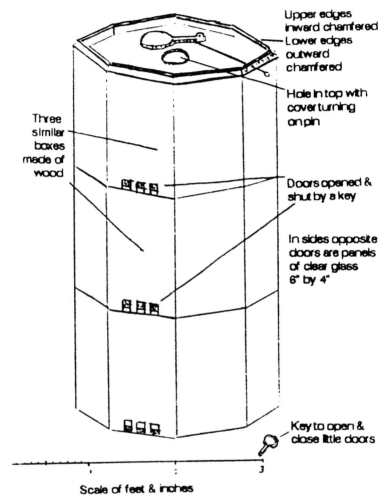

Upper edges
inward chamfered
Lower edges
outward
chamfered

Hole in top with
cover turning
on pin

Three
similar
boxes
made of
wood

Doors opened &
shut by a key

In sides opposite
doors are panels
of clear glass
6" by 4"

Key to open &
close little doors

Scale of feet & inches

Drawn by C. Wren at Oxford in 1654. Used in Samuel Hartlib's book 'The Reformed Commonwealth of Bees' publ. in 1655. A very similar drawing also appears in a paper presented to the Royal Society at Gresham's College, London in 1673.

CHAPTER THREE

THE REV. JOHN THORLEY, M.A. 1671–1759

The Rev. John Thorley kept bees in the first half of the 18th century, spanning the reigns of Queen Anne and the first two Georges. He is chiefly remembered for his book 'Female Monarchy', published in 1744 after 'forty years of observation and experience', as he put it himself. He was the first to observe and record the eight wax platelets in pockets of the abdomens of young worker bees. The first serious studies of wax platelets and their secretion was not made until some years later (John Hunter 1792, Francis Huber 1793). At a time when most beekeepers were still speaking (as Shakespeare did) of bees being led by a King or Prince, Thorley removed all doubt by recording his experience of a Queen laying her eggs on his hand as she walked across it, hence the title of his book. He regularly found and handled queen bees at a time when very few beekeepers had ever seen one, in the days before moveable frame hives. So far as I am aware, he was the first to describe not only the treble piping of young virgins running free in the hive, but also the deep bass notes of a queen not yet emerged from her ripe cell.

He was also the first beekeeper, so far as I can trace, to realize that bees can recognize colour and make use of this fact. In his own words 'Forget not to paint the mouths of your colonies with different colours, as Red, White, Blue, Yellow etc. in the form of a half-moon or square, that the bees may know their own home.'

Bee Anaesthetic

His 'secret' was the use of smoke from a dried fungus, used as a narcotic to calm, and even anaesthetize a hive of bees. Variously called 'frog cheese', 'pug foist', 'puck' or just 'giant fungus' (today more commonly called 'puff-ball'), he describes how he obtained them (as large as a man's head sometimes) from shepherds and farm workers. When fresh, they could be sliced and cooked something like mushrooms but on drying in summer or in a slow oven the fungus went brown and finally consisted of a fine powder in a tough outer skin. He describes taking a piece the size of a hen's egg on a stick and holding it smouldering slowly under a skep of bees so that the smoke and fumes went up into the colony (no purpose-made smokers in those days). In a minute the bees would drop off the comb like hail, into an empty skep, and wake up apparently none the worse an hour or two later. He used this technique to harvest honeycombs from skeps and box hives (instead of killing the bees with burning sulphur), and to unite two or three stocks with no fighting. He would also examine the bees, identify the queen (usually the last to fall down), even count and weigh them to arrive at the number in a swarm or weighing one pound. An illustration in his book shows him seated at the study table, making a detailed examination of a number of anaesthetized bees. Some years ago I found two or three of these fungi, the size of a man's head, dried them all summer in the greenhouse and successfully used a small piece of the brown matter wrapped in hessian in my smoker, to control the occasional colony of very aggressive bees. I have hesitated to speak much about this, for fear that young people might wish to experiment with it, as a narcotic drug, on themselves.

Bee House

John Thorley advocated the use of bee houses, and in his book there is an illustration of an open-fronted wooden bee house with five octagonal hives (like those mentioned in the article on Rev. John Wilkins). However, he kept his own bees for the most part in straw skeps. Those of us fortunate enough to have been on the Devon Beekeepers' annual visits to Germany will recall very similar bee houses in use today in the Tyrol, and of course elsewhere in Europe.

A Famous Swarm

Perhaps Thorley's ability as a practical beekeeper is best illustrated by his own story of finding two queens in a swarm which had settled on the face and chest of his maidservant Anne Herbert in 1717. A

Rev. J. Thorley in his study

swarm had been found in the close, twisted branches of a codling apple tree and was proving difficult to take. He persuaded her to hold the skep above her head while he climbed the tree and brushed or shook the bees off. She was 'protected' by a linen cloth draped over her head and shoulders. Unfortunately the main body of the cluster fell, not into the skep but on her head, and soon the bees crawled up under the cloth and reformed on her chin and breast. To her great credit she stood firm and did not scream or panic. Thorley quickly found the queen and dropped her into the skep, plus some bees, expecting the rest of the bees to follow, but they did not. Whereupon he tried again, found a second queen and put her also into the skep. Within two or three minutes all the bees followed and not a single bee remained on Anne, nor had she received a single sting. What a popular demonstration this would be today at Stoneleigh!

Anne became very interested in beekeeping and for many years thereafter 'resolutely helped him in the most hazardous services'.

In 1744 she was living in a cottage at Little Rissington in Gloucestershire, about seven or eight miles away from the vicarage at Chipping Norton. On many occasions she confirmed the truth of this story to readers of his book who doubted. Lucky John Thorley!

John Thorley was the Presbyterian Minister of Chipping Norton from 1699 to 1759; a memorial tablet in the wall of the present Baptist Church, New Street, records his 60 year ministry but pays no tribute to his fame as a beekeeper.

CHAPTER FOUR

ANTON JANSCHA 1734–1773

His claim to fame rests on three major points:
  i) that he was almost certainly the first man to be appointed specifically as a full-time, paid beekeeping lecturer,
  ii) that in 1771, some 20 years before the letters of Huber were published, he explained in detail the mating flight of a virgin

queen and described the 'mating sign' to be seen attached to the tip of her abdomen. He also referred to a queen mating with several drones,

iii) that in the words of a well-known beekeeping historian, the late Dr Malcolm Fraser: 'If anyone has written a better or more comprehensive book than Janscha's on the swarming of bees, I do not know it.'

The Man

Anton was the eldest of three talented brothers, born into the family of a small farmer and beekeeper in Carinthia, the south eastern province of Austria bordering on what used to be called Jugoslavia. His father had a high reputation as a good beekeeper but, above all, in the decorative painting of houses so beloved of Austrians then and still seen today. Anton's progress owed much to the enlightened Empress of Austria, the renowned Maria Theresa who, in 1766 instituted an engraving school in the Art Academy of Vienna and awarded scholarships to Anton and his brothers Laurence and Valentine.

Anton received a subsistence allowance of three hundred and sixty gulden* a year and his brothers two hundred and forty each. Within eighteen months, Anton won the senior Academy Award, enabling him to study Art in Italy, but before he could go, he applied for and was appointed to the post of Beekeeping Instructor at the College of Beekeeping, founded in Vienna to encourage beekeeping in Austria. He was allowed to retain his Academy subsistence allowance, plus an additional fifty gulden a month. His clearly defined main duty was to give public lectures and demonstrations in the Augarten in Vienna daily from May to mid-September, also to receive and instruct visitors and help them with their beekeeping problems. During the weeks when buckwheat was in flower, the school hives were moved to farm sites and instruction carried out there. It is very clear that Maria Theresa herself took a personal interest, and Anton frequently demonstrated to her court, much as John Wildman was doing at the same time (1768–1770) before the court of George III in England. In 1770 Anton was also appointed

*Equivalent to a florin or Dutch guilder.

Imperial Beekeeper to Her Majesty, at an enhanced salary, and a year later he published his first book 'Handling Bee Swarms' and was given a full-time assistant lecturer.

Sadly he died of typhus fever in 1773, and his only other book, a larger and general account of beekeeping, was published posthumously from his notes. His brother Laurence became a professor of Artistic Studies in the Academy of Vienna and survived until 1812.

His Beekeeping

Janscha used wooden rectangular bee boxes of about 45 litre capacity, made of $\frac{3}{4}$ inch thick spruce boards. Internal measurements were 31 inches (79 cm) long by $14\frac{1}{4}$ inches (37 cm) wide. Depth varied, but was normally $6\frac{1}{4}$ inches (16 cm). No mention was made in his books of either frames or top bars. In the upper board or crown board was a square 4 inch side hole having a sliding cover which could be opened or closed at will, to enable a second box to be used as a super. The two end boards were not nailed on but just slipped into the two long side boards, and taken out for access when required. The rear end board was also cut so as to slide into the hive to lessen the space, for a small swarm. The main dimensions were standardized as he piled them together, usually to form the side of a bee house, with rear access within the house. As the drawing of his bee house in the Vienna Augarten shows, thirty of these Bauernkasten hives could be operated in one small hut.

His smoker consisted of a vessel of sheet iron or clay which fitted on the end of a bellows. He devised queen cages woven from fine wire, or made of wood with a line of holes for ventilation and feeding by workers. At first he used the small cages which held crickets (grasshoppers) at that time; these were commonly kept in homes for their cheerful chirps. Later, he adapted similar cages specially for holding and introducing queens. For brushing bees off combs a bunch of feathers, and for quietening bees on combs a water syringe with a fine spray, were employed. He spoke of the need always to have available clean, empty hives, and used 'starters' of drawn comb supported as shown in the drawing. This usually ensured that the bees built parallel combs as required.

Special Techniques

His management encouraged swarming and the collection of swarms, but he also described clearly the method of making artificial swarms, of making three colonies from two, even of making up a new stock with combs from several hives.

His queen-raising was very simple. He took three or four handfuls of bees from a strong hive and ladled them into an empty one; then he inserted a nice piece of newly built comb, cut out of the same, or another hive. The cells had to contain very small, scarcely visible larvae laying in pools of glistening liquid. The comb had to be no bigger than the bees could easily cover and keep warm. It was kept upright in a stand made of a piece of wood with a withy (flexible willow twig) bent into the shape of a bow on each side (see drawing). A comb of honey was also placed inside and the entrance closed for a few days, to prevent the bees from returning home. According to Anton, the queen would emerge from her cell in about twelve days and was allowed to continue living in the small hive with its few bees until mated, and was then placed in a queen cage whenever needed. He made the point that a fertile queen can be freely introduced into any hive which has lost a queen, two hours after the loss. Otherwise she should be introduced first in a cage. A virgin queen must always be introduced in a cage, and she is usually accepted after four or five days. A queen cell with a little adherent wax can be given to a swarm without a queen.

General Comment

Much more could be written, but must be left. Obviously Anton was a supremely skilful manipulator of bees, and his early death a great loss to the craft. How fortunate he was to have lived in Austria during the reign of that enlightened monarch, the Empress Maria Theresa, who clearly understood the value of bees and beekeeping, and had the power to support and encourage teachers to spread their skills.

Nothing to do with beekeeping, but her financial acumen was also unusual, and her silver dollars gained respect for a long time over a wide area. As recently as the 1939–45 War, small bags of Maria

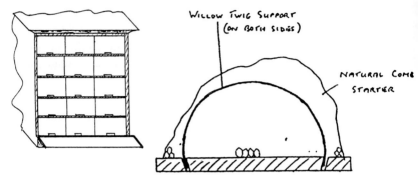

Janscha's Bee House in Augarten, after woodcut in 'Aghandlung von Schwarmen Der Bienen' 1771. Right-hand drawing shows his queen rearing strip.

Theresa silver dollars were used by our Intelligence officers working in Abyssinia and other African areas of conflict behind the lines. Would that our government were as enlightened as that noble lady!

CHAPTER FIVE

THOMAS WILDMAN
1734–1781

Apart from his book 'A Treatise on the Management of Bees' published in 1768, Thomas Wildman is chiefly remembered by the way in which he made beekeeping interesting to so many people, from the court of King George III and Queen Charlotte down to the humblest citizen.

He not only gave public performances of his mastery over bees by making them go backwards and forwards from one hive to another, but also attracted bees to cluster on his chin like a beard.

He even made swarms of bees follow him around a circus ring while galloping on horseback, until they finally clustered on his shoulder while he was still moving.

Little is known of his early days except that he was Devon born and spent the first part of his life in Plymouth. John Mills in his 'Essay on the Management of Bees' published in 1766 referred to Wildman, the Plymouth bee-man, who made swarms follow him. As his almost supernatural skill became more widely known, he sought his fortune in London in 1766, and in 1768 not only received the patronage of King George III but published his 'Treatise on the Management of Bees' which he dedicated to Queen Charlotte.

His popularity may be judged from the fact that nearly 500 people paid for his book before he even wrote it, and the subscription list included the King and Queen, the Dukes of Norfolk, Portland, etc. the Earls of Essex, Coventry, etc. Also scores of other titled people, professors, clergymen, architects, postmasters, army officers. Fellows of the Royal Society, hosiers, linen drapers, coffee house proprietors and so on. The worlds of fashion, intellect and business were interested in beekeeping as never before or since. Although so talented on the public relations side, he was much more than a circus performer or the equivalent of a pop-star and in his book there is evidence of wide reading of the books available at that time, from the classics to Hartlib, Thorley *et al*, even of French authors like Mme Vicat.

Wildman evolved a management system which did not involve killing bees. As he says in Chapter Five of his book 'Were we to kill the hen for her egg, the cow for her milk, or the sheep for the fleece it bears, everyone would instantly see how much we should act contrary to our own interests: and yet this is practised every year, in our inhuman and impolitic slaughter of the bees.'

His beekeeping was based on the use of four or more flat-topped skeps per stock, each skep being about 10 inches wide by 7 inches high internally, about two gallons in volume. In summer the pile of four skeps would have seemed to the bees not unlike a hollow tree and had the advantage that about 20 pounds of honey could be taken off the top without killing the bees. Not having modern clearer boards he would, in his own words ' ... take away the top hive at noon on a fair day, and if any bees remain on it, turn it up some distance from the stand and strike it upon the sides, the bees will be alarmed, take wing and re-join their family.'

He would start with a good swarm put into one hive, with a cover over it. Next morning, or as soon as combs were being built, he would place a second skep beneath the first. In his own words, 'The queen will lay some eggs in the upper hive; but so soon as the lower hive is filled with combs, she will lay most of them in it. In little more than three weeks, all the eggs laid in the upper hive will be turned to bees, and if the season is favourable, their cells will soon be filled with honey. So soon as they want room, a third hive should be placed under the two former, and in a few days after the end of three weeks from the time the swarm was put into the hive, the top hive may be taken away at noon of a fair day; and cleared of bees as already explained.'

'So soon as the hives seem to be again crowded and the upper hive is well stored, or filled with honey, a fourth hive should be placed under the third and the upper hive be taken off the next fair day at noon, and treated as already directed. If the season is very favourable, the bees may still fill another hive. In this case the honey may be taken out of the second hive which can then be placed under the fourth. In the month of September the top hive should be examined, and if full, it will be a sufficient provision for the winter: but if it contain less than twenty pounds of honey, then in the month of October the lower hive should be removed and one of the spare hives taken away during summer should be put on the remaining one, to supply the bees with abundant provision for the winter.'

Here is a logical management system in which bees are steadily building combs downwards, as they would be in nature, and storing honey in the upper parts of the combs, which can be taken off during the summer. The bees live on and are well provided for in winter; he considered a skep containing 20 pounds of honey to be sufficient. He made some shrewd comments on winter mortality, for example, '... many hives of bees thought to die of cold in winter, in truth die of famine, as was the case in 1759 when the constant rain in summer hindered the bees from laying in a sufficient store of provisions.'

A Description of Wildman's Straw Hive (in his own words)

In the upper row of straw there is a hoop of about half an inch in breadth to which are nailed five bars of deal, a full quarter of an inch in thickness and an inch and a quarter wide, and half an inch asunder from each other; a narroe short bar is nailed at each side, half an inch distant from the bars next them, in order to fill up the remaining part of the circle, so that there are in all seven bars of deal to which the bees fix their combs.

A circular cover of straw a foot in diameter, so that it may be the same width as the outside of the hive, with a coat of cow- dung (least apt to crack). For winter this cover can be made fast to the hive with a needle and pack-thread, so that neither cold nor vermin may enter.

Wildman preferred dry mead and used rather less honey than most, in order that the honey might '... be fermented right out, and the liquor acquire a fine, racy flavour.' To preserve the true aroma he boiled the liquor only a very short time with some white of egg to bring out particles of wax, bee bread, etc. before scumming off and fermenting.

Although he used mostly skeps he made and sold wooden bee boxes and recommended that they be made of red cedar. His nephew Daniel later took over the hive-making side of the business and became the first English full-time professional appliance maker, having a shop in Holborn until his death in 1809. Thus we see how the English started using expensive red cedar while the rest of the world used cheaper woods: it was his connection with the wealthy aristocracy who kept bees and wanted only the best! Incidentally, a footnote to the list of subscribers says: 'If any subscribers do not choose to manage their bees themselves, Mr. Wildman will undertake it for the yearly sum of three guineas.' Can any reader suggest what 3 guineas in 1768 would be equivalent to today?

CHAPTER SIX

REV. JACOB ISAAC 1750–1818

Jacob Isaac was the Unitarian Minister at Moretonhampstead in Devon from 1780 until his death in 1818. He is remembered chiefly as founder and secretary of the Western Apiarian Society, the first society or club of beekeepers on record in Britain, but also for his flat-topped skep (the 'Moreton Hive') and for his book 'The General Apiarian'.

The Western Apiarian Society was founded in 1795 with stated objects: 'To promote knowledge of the best method of managing bees, to encourage fresh discoveries concerning them and their use to the greatest interest of the community, especially of cottagers.' With life membership at five guineas and annual subscription of half a guinea, members were mostly aristocratic or professional. In 1800 over forty strong, they included Viscount Courtenay, Lord Clifford,

Sir Lawrence Palk M.P., James Templar of Stover, Mr J. Pud-
dicombe (surgeon) and Rev. Isaac (secretary). The expression 'cottager' was still in use in 1913 in the Devon Beekeepers' Association,
with annual membership costing five shillings but only half a crown
for cottagers. The Society met every quarter in the Globe Tavern,
Exeter, and after each meeting the 'Transactions of the Western
Apiarian Society' were fully reported in the local press; the last full
meeting was on 6 October 1808, after which the Society was
apparently dissolved. The venue survived as the Globe Hotel until
destroyed by enemy bombs in 1942.

   One of the main objects was to teach methods of taking honey
without killing bees over a sulphur pit. One method recommended
was to drive or drum the bees from an inverted full skep into an
empty one at the end of July, and after removing honeycombs from
the sides, to run the bees back and feed sugar syrup (or take the bees
to Dartmoor for heather honey). Another method was 'storifying', or
using two or three Moreton hives on top of one another, so that at
the end of the season the top one, or even two, might contain just
honeycombs. Various research projects were carried out by groups
of members, who reported back to the next quarterly meeting. One
such, under Isaac's direction, was concerned with moving hives
various distances up to six miles, and noting whether the bees
returned to their old site. They found that more returned if the
hives were moved during the day, and fewer if moved at dusk: that
a number of bees returned when moved a mile but that this soon
became insignificant at greater distances. Their final conclusion was
that hive moving should be done at dusk and to distances well over
a mile away. The Society also investigated the use of pugfoist smoke
(from dried giant puff-balls), the production of queens from common
eggs by extending the common cells containing them, and noting
whether a hive had a queen or not by external indications.

   Prizes or premiums were offered for the largest honey yields
obtained without killing bees. In the year 1800 Mr Wotton (also of
Moretonhampstead) obtained $146\frac{1}{2}$ pounds of rich honeycombs yield-
ing 120 pounds of pure honey from one stock of bees given other
skeps as supers, and also to one side as collaterals with a connecting
passage. He estimated that at the height of the season the bees and

combs occupied three bushels (about 110 litres, equivalent to a National brood box plus four or five supers today). We glibly speak of the old English black bees as being much less prolific than our modern bees, but Mr Wotton's were certainly prolific. Probably 1800 was a good bee year, as Isaac himself obtained 556 pounds of honey from fourteen hives without killing any bees. At this time he had mostly small cottage skeps, but some storified hives; his largest 'take' was 74 pounds.

There was a special class for cottagers who could prove that they had, in one season, taken from their bees the value of one year's rent of their houses and gardens, in honey and swarms, without destroying any bees. In 1803 Mr D. Rowe of Cornwall won the main Premium of £4 in this class.

The Moreton Hive was made of straw, bound with bramble splits, cylindrical in shape with diameter of 12 inches, 6 inches high and flat-topped. In volume slightly larger than Wildman's hive (2·4 gallons against 2 gallons), with two or three such hives per stock. At the top of each hive was a round deal board 14 inches in diameter and at least $\frac{1}{2}$ inch thick, rounded at the edge to fit the hive. Into this round board a number of $\frac{1}{2}$ inch slots were cut to within an inch of the circumference to leave bars of width $1\frac{1}{8}$ inch, on which thin strips of wood coated with wax were tacked for the bees to attach their combs. The base was a narrow wooden hoop with holes to receive the bramble stitches of the first round of straw. Each hoop was mortised exactly $\frac{1}{4}$ inch up from the lower edge to give an entrance $2\frac{1}{2} \times \frac{1}{4}$ inch.

'The General Apiarian' of 128 pages, 12 mo., (7 × 4 inches) was published in 1803 by Trewmans of Exeter. I had the privilege of reading Isaac's personal copy, which is in the Methodist Library, Gordon Square, London. It dealt with many topics including his own flat-topped skep (the Moreton hive) and also with a most unusual double skep called the 'Preserver and Remunerator', i.e. brood box and honey chamber, invented by James Roberts of Crediton.

Isaac's technique with late swarms was to take them to nearby Dartmoor for the heather and he wrote of one July swarm which weighed only 5 pounds 9 ounces on 30 July when it was taken up on the moor; when brought back in late September it weighed 30 pounds 1 ounce. On this topic Rev. Isaac commented that he had reason to believe that all heather honey came in during August. He also wrote of the value of gaining winter stores from ivy late in the year.

He related how Mr Dawe of Buckland Monachorum had a full hive with bees hanging outside on the 1 August 1801, when a pig knocked the hive over and some combs fell on the ground, with many bees staying clustered on them. He placed a skep over them and in a few days they ascended. By 26 September both stocks were well provided for the winter and showed every sign of having queens. This could presumably be called the 'Pig Method' of making increase!

His own recipe for mead was as follows: 'take 1 lb. honey per quart of water, boil for fifteen minutes and take off the scum. Add 1 oz. of fine hops per gallon, boil again for ten minutes, run through a fine linen surplice. Cool and tun; three weeks later bung down. Bottle at twelve months and drink after three years.' Presumably the same tun or barrel was used over and over again and retained enough natural yeast to start up a new fermentation.

The Rev. Isaac's obituary in 'The Monthly Repository' records his death on 2 December 1818 and spoke of his 'Simplicity of manner, his zeal in the cause of his Divine Master, his generous regard for the poor, and resignation amidst agonies that human skill could neither remove nor soften.'

CHAPTER SEVEN

FRANCIS HUBER 1750–1831

Blind from early childhood after a series of accidents, this Swiss beekeeper directed the observations of others and methodically investigated almost every possible aspect of bee behaviour, most intensively between 1787 and 1793, but also for several years after that. His constant companion for 15 years was his man-servant Francis Burnens, of humble birth and with no formal education. Much of the credit for Huber's work could fairly be shared with Burnens, who is recorded on one occasion as working for 24 hours without food or rest to 'catch laying workers actually laying eggs'. If genius be a compound of inspiration and perspiration, the faithful Burnens certainly provided the latter. He also enlisted the aid of Mlle Jurine, a competent naturalist, Maria his wife, and later of his son Pierre, an authority on 'Habits of Ants' in his own right.

He is remembered chiefly for his ingenious 'Leaf Hive' which enabled any brood comb out of 12 to be investigated and closely observed at any time: this was 60 years before Langstroth and the introduction of modern types of moveable frames in hives.

The model illustrated has 12 frames each measuring $12 \times 9\frac{1}{2}$ inches, hinged together at the back but in the text Huber says he made frames of pine 12×12 inches. Huber wrote that the boards inserted between frames 6 and 7 were only used when making an artificial swarm, by splitting the hive into two equal parts.

When stocking a hive with a swarm, small pieces of drawn comb were inserted at the tops of frames to guide the bees to draw combs in the frames provided. Hives were left alone for three days before opening up to correct any misplaced combs. Normally only the lower entrances at 2 and 11 were open, but the others could be opened or closed at will.

Even a brief summary of his work would take up far more space than is available for this article, but the shortest list would have to include queen mating, queen introduction and combat between queens, laying workers, wax glands, wax production and comb building, the distances flown by bees, the incidence and behaviour of swarms, at the very least. As a sample of his work, just one topic is now considered in some depth.

Beeswax; Production and Use by Bees

At this time authors were still writing about wax being produced from the loads of pollen brought into a hive. Huber first tested this theory in 1793, when on 24 May a swarm which had just left the parent stock was lodged in a new hive, the entrance closed and the colony taken into a cool dark cellar and fed with honey and water. After two days they were allowed to fly in a closed apartment (but not to forage) while the hive was examined, and found to have five fine combs of new, white wax. This suggested that wax was made from honey, but Huber considered that the bees might have had some pollen in their stomachs, so after removing all five combs Burnens made the bees return to the hive, again fed them honey and water while confined in the cellar. After three days there were five more combs, similar to those previously removed. Under exactly similar conditions this experiment was repeated with the same bees yet again, with no access to pollen but amply fed with honey and water. Each time they produced new wax combs. After this they were generously fed with pollen and water for eight days, yet made no wax at all. It seems probable that the pollen fed to the bees contained a certain amount of honey, perhaps just enough to sustain life.

In order to obviate the possibility that there may have been some wax particles in the honey, the experiment was repeated with three swarms, all in glass hives, two fed with a pound of sugar dissolved in water and the third with a pound of honey. Wax was produced in all three cases, in somewhat greater abundance by those fed on sugar syrup. The experiment was repeated seven times. The greatest quantity of wax obtained from a pound of sugar was $2\frac{3}{4}$ ounces i.e. a pound of wax from just under 6 pounds of sugar. As one might expect, rather more honey was taken, and assuming a water content of c.18% one would expect a figure of about 7 pounds, which was what Huber found. Even during the last year (1993) I have read current articles in which the writers loosely refer to 'the quantity of up to 20 lb. honey' needed to produce a single pound of beeswax!

Field Tests

In 1793 Huber was operating sixty-five hives, and this was a year of high temperatures and great drought throughout July and August, with no rain for six weeks prior to 10 August, and none again after 14 August for another three weeks; rather like 1990 in fact! When his hives were closely examined at the end of August it became evident that all had stored a great deal of pollen but scarcely any honey. There was no new wax in any hive. No combs had been enlarged, even those of late swarms remained only partly built. Once again the connection between income and honey and wax comb-building was demonstrated.

Wax Secretion

In this same year Huber accurately described the secretion of wax platelets in pairs on the under surfaces of four abdominal rings. He found that these scales dissolved completely in spirit of turpentine, whereas the whitest fragments of newly worked combs dissolved but left insoluble particles. From this he deduced that bees added some matter when working the wax scales to produce comb. He commissioned Mlle Jurine to dissect under the wax membranes (called mirrors now), but no direct communication between them and the abdomen below could be discovered. However, when the membrane was pierced by a fine needle, some transparent fluid appeared, which coagulated on cooling to a substance resembling wax, and again liquefied on exposure to heat, just as the tiny wax scales themselves did when teased from the abdominal plates of a wax-working bee. He conjectured that the stomach juices transuded through very thin integuments to traverse the membrane. No-one got further with this for another 180 years and then only with the aid of an electron microscope.

Like a true scientist Huber was scrupulously fair and gave full credit to his English contemporary John Hunter F.R.S., even having translated extracts of his beeswax paper (Phil. Trans.) into French. Hunter had expressed his opinion that there could not be enough wax arising from these tiny scales alone and suggested that much pollen had to be added. The credit for quantifying the situation by laboratory and field work must go to Huber.

Huber was never content with mere anecdotal evidence, his approach was strictly scientific, with an insistence on controls and endless repetition before he came to any conclusion. His work would have been outstanding had he enjoyed all normal senses, but to have achieved what he did, as a blind man 200 years ago, makes him unique.

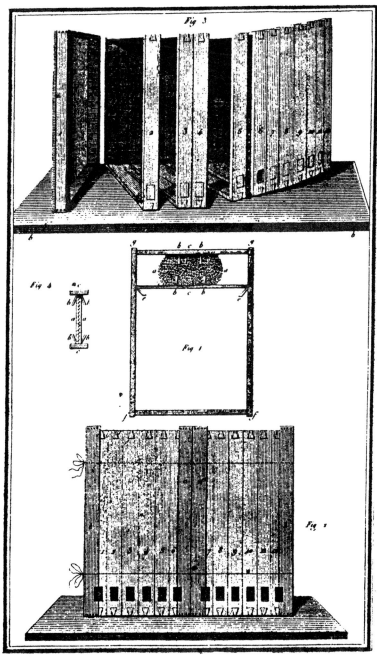

Huber's leafhive

Much of Huber's work was originally written up in a series of very long letters to his friend M. C. Bonnet, the celebrated naturalist who died in 1793.

The first volume of his work *Nouvelles Observations sur les Abeilles* was published in Geneva in 1792, and the second (edited by his son Pierre) was published in Geneva in 1814. The first English translation 'New Observations on Bees' was published in Edinburgh in 1806, but the first to cover all his work, though somewhat abridged, was the third edition published in Edinburgh in 1821. These brief notes have been compiled after reference to the two volumes in the original French as well as to the 1821 translation. The 1926 edition contains ten additional chapters by Pierre Huber.

CHAPTER EIGHT

DR EDWARD BEVAN 1770–1860

Dr Bevan was born in London, but as an infant lost his father and was brought up in Hereford by his mother, living with her father Mr Powles. He was educated from the early age of eight at Wotton-under-Edge Grammar School, and four years later at the College School, Hereford. His uncle, Mr Powles (a surgeon at Wotton) persuaded him to study medicine, which he did under the famous Abernethy and others. After practising at Mortlake, Stoke-upon-Trent and Congleton (Cheshire) for a total of about twenty years his health gave way and he retired to a small estate at Bridstow, near Ross in Herefordshire, where he took up beekeeping.

Although most of his personal observations relate to Herefordshire, he kept in close touch with six or seven other beekeepers whose education matched his own and who lived as far apart as Dumfriesshire, Edinburgh, Kent, Worcester, Leicester and Hampshire. At this time there were no regular beekeeping journals, but articles dealing with bees were published from time to time in botanical and gardening journals. Bevan's book was published in 1827, but he is best known for the 1838 edition of 'The Honey Bee, its Natural History, Physiology and Management'. Some old bee books are interesting on account of their age, but Bevan can be read with advantage today. For example, his advice on choice of apiary sites is as valid now, as it was over one hundred and fifty years ago. He covered the need to be close to a stream or pond, or else to provide a shallow pan of water with sticks or stones to prevent bees drowning. He made the point of being close to ample forage such as clover, buckwheat and 'saintfoin', with access to the rear of hives for easy inspection; also that hives should be on stands at least 18 inches off the ground, and having a gentle forward slope. Practical points such as screening from strong winds, having a southerly aspect, not close to a public footpath, not crowded too closely together, were all covered. For his own home apiary he built a bee house of timber and thatch on a brick base, measuring 7 feet square internally, to take seven stocks, and attached great importance to the ability to watch his bees every day without having to travel.

He took careful note of the flora available to bees in his area, and it so closely resembles that in the south-west today as to be worth quoting, in his order: 'From laurestinus in late winter to willow and gooseberry in spring, followed by apple, currants, maple, sycamore, clover, lime, extra-floral nectaries of field beans, mustard and the brassica tribe generally, buckwheat, holly, bramble, rosemary, borage, thyme and teazle, willowherb, heather, furze, broom and finally ivy at the end of October, especially valuable for its pollen.' He mentioned honeydew in mid-July from limes and oaks, especially the Holm Oak.

On the scientific side he read widely and was well aware of Huber and the work of his microscopist Mlle Jurine of Geneva. He agreed with his friend Mr Dobbs that ' . . . a queen has intercourse with several drones, that there might be a sufficient deposition of sperm to impregnate all her eggs'. He also found by personal observation that unless a queen was impregnated within three weeks, she would become a drone-layer. He understood and explained the difference between royal jelly and worker brood food, the former having a more pungent taste as well as being more profusely supplied. He realized that pollen was pre-digested by the nurse bees, not just fed as raw pollen. Here is the evidence of a trained and scholarly mind at work, before the age of moveable frame hives.

Bevan used bee boxes about 12 inches square × 9 inches deep, made of inch-thick red cedar. Each box had seven bars $1\frac{1}{8}$ inch wide × $\frac{1}{2}$ inch thick, from which combs were built. The three central bars were close-spaced at $\frac{7}{16}$ inch and the outer bars more widely spaced at $\frac{9}{16}$ inch. He insisted that all bars should be of an exact length, so that any bar would fit into any hive. In the absence of wax foundation in those days, Bevan used small pieces of drawn comb fastened below alternate top bars, to act as guides and prevent combs being built at awkward angles across more than one frame. These boxes were used in tiers ('storified' as Bevan said) one above the other, with a substantial cover board on the topmost. The entrance was cut into the thickness of a very solid floor. If an additional box were added below it was called 'nadiring'; if placed above, it was called 'supering'. He preferred to super, as we do today. Bevan gave credit to Mr Golding (of Hunton near Maidstone) for the first use of a crown board with either one large hole or three small ones, to take glass jars which the bees would fill with pure honeycombs. In 1974 I tried this and obtained a large glass bell-jar full of natural honeycomb, which I exhibited at Devon County Show and elsewhere for three years. When finally cut out and eaten (or sold in 8 ounce containers) I obtained $14\frac{1}{2}$ pounds of fine comb honey.

Of course, in 1830 the principle of the bee space had not been discovered, so Bevan had the inconvenience of cutting through brace comb attached to the hive sides before he could take a comb out for inspection.

There were no purpose-built smokers in those days, but Bevan made for himself a 'fumigating box' with bellows and used tobacco smoke to control his bees during manipulations such as making artificial swarms, lifting up combs attached to bars to find queens and queen cells. Bevan also had some common straw skeps and used these with top-bars of varying length; he commented that wooden bee boxes were much better for storifying.

Bevan was one of the first to describe accurately the two quite different sounds made by young queens. He spoke of the sharp, clear high notes as from a flute, made by a young princess at liberty in the hive, contrasted with the hoarse, low-pitched series of short croaks made by a princess still confined in her cell.

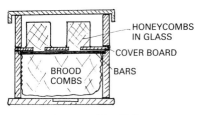

Dr Bevan's square hive 1848

Accepting that he lived a hundred years before most of the great fundamental research that we now have access to, Bevan learnt by patient observation and trial and error many things which have since been attributed to modern bee scientists. He was years ahead of his time and his original book is still valuable for its content, quite apart from its value as an antique.

CHAPTER NINE

REV. LORENZO L. LANGSTROTH 1810–1895

Perhaps the greatest possible tribute to this supreme bee master is the fact that over three-quarters of all the hives in the world today are Langstroth hives.

From China to Mexico, from Australia and New Zealand to Brazil and Argentina, his hives are used so completely that even the name has dropped out, and it is sufficient just to say 'hive', it being taken for granted that it is a Langstroth. In smaller beekeeping countries too, (Britain, France, Sweden) where a variety of different hives are still found, they all use and take for granted the principle of the 'bee space' of about $\frac{1}{4}$ inch to $\frac{5}{16}$ inch (7 mm). This, as Langstroth discovered in 1851, allows hanging frames to be lifted up for inspection, use or replacement. Any space larger than this is filled with natural comb, and any smaller is filled with propolis, or bee gum, gluing the surfaces together.

The Man

With insular pride we can almost claim him as a Yorkshireman, for his grandfather, Thomas Langstroth, emigrated to America in 1767 from Horton-in-Ribblesdale, where the River Wharf rises in a small mountain valley called Langstrothdale in the West Riding. His forebears farmed there for generations.

Lorenzo Lorraine Langstroth graduated from Yale in 1831 and continued his studies there at the Divinity School, supporting himself by teaching and then for two more years remained as a mathematics tutor, before being called to the Ministry of the Congregational Church. He was already suffering from a malady (which he called 'head trouble') which was to afflict him throughout his long life, taking the form of intense depression and melancholia which made him incapable of work for long periods.

For the rest of his life he alternately taught and preached, became a respected school principal or a well-loved pastor, but was forced to resign over and over again on grounds of ill-health. When able to work he was so outstanding that his classes and congregations loved him and preferred him to all others. Finally, he collapsed and died in church, while taking a service, on Sunday, 6 October 1895.

From the age of six, he had been fascinated by insects, kept flies in paper cages and even wore out the knees of his breeches watching and playing with ants in the garden. Not until 1848 did he start beekeeping.

The Beekeeper

As a scholar of outstanding ability, Langstroth read and collected bee books, but praised most highly Francis Huber's 'New Observations on Bees' (1821 edn) and Dr Edward Bevan's 'The Honey Bee' (1838 edn). Having started with a log hive, he soon acquired two bar hives, (Dr Bevan's design), in which the bees built combs down from wooden top bars but, of course, also attached the combs to the sides of the hives. These hives had wooden cover boards very much like our crown boards, but with three or four holes on which glass vessels were placed for the bees to fill with comb honey. (Using Bevan's hives, 18 inches square × 6 inches deep, he won a First Prize for comb honey in glass in 1850). The problem was to remove the cover boards when they were stuck down with propolis. In order to save the labour of forcing off stuck-down cover boards, Langstroth experimented by cutting rabbets in hive ends $\frac{3}{8}$ inch deeper, so that the top bars were then this distance down from the cover. To his delight, in the summer of 1851, he was able to lift off the cover boards plus glasses of honeycomb with very little trouble, in fact he had achieved what we now call a 'top bee space'. For weeks after this he pondered on what could be done to stop the brood combs being stuck to the hive walls. On 30 October 1851, on the way home from his apiary two miles away, he suddenly thought, 'Why not enclose the combs in complete frames having $\frac{3}{8}$ inch gap between frame sides and hive end walls?' He felt that he had the answer and said in his book, 'The Hive and the Honey Bee' that he felt like Archimedes and wanted to run through the streets shouting 'Eureka'.

That night he sat up late discussing this idea with his friend the Rev. Sanders, and making sketches. He realized that the same idea should work with supers also. Unfortunately, it was too late in the year to try it out, but early in January 1852 he applied for a patent, sold the goodwill of his school and gave up teaching. Early in that spring, he made up a set of frames and fitted them with small pieces of guide comb. The very first day that it was warm enough for the bees to fly, he shook off old combs into his new frame hive and found that his new idea really worked. During that summer, he made up over 100 moveable frame hives and sold most of them, with the right to use his patent frame with the $\frac{1}{4}$ to $\frac{3}{8}$ inch bee space.

Sadly, during that summer, he suffered a serious nervous breakdown and had to sell off his stocks.

The Langstroth Hive and Frame

Despite the oft-repeated story of his casual use of a champagne case, the true origin of this hive, with the odd measurement ($18\frac{1}{8} \times 14\frac{1}{8}$ inches) was in fact quite different. Langstroth was a great admirer of Dr Edward Bevan, of Herefordshire, and had closely studied the 1838 edition of his book 'The Honey Bee', so he made his first bar hive 18 inches square, like Bevan's. In order to observe what was going on in his first two hives, he made them of glass, and the standard American sheet of glass at that time measured 12×18 inches from which he cut two panels, each 6×18 inches giving a hive 6 inches deep. He then came to realize the value of a dead air space as opposed to two sheets of glass just placed together, and separated the panes by the insertion of narrow strips of wood veneer $\frac{1}{16}$ inch thick on all sides, for better insulation.

In 1852, he reduced the hive width by 4 inches and increased the depth by the same amount, reasoning that bees would over-winter better on fewer but larger frames. Once factories set their standards and mass-produced his frames and bee boxes, the dimensions became fixed, so far as the $18\frac{1}{8} \times 14\frac{1}{8}$ inches was concerned, although since then, boxes of varying depth have been made. From 1853 his hives were all made of wood instead of glass, and to allow for timber shrinkage after manufacture, the slightly larger $18\frac{5}{16} \times 14\frac{5}{16}$ inch standard became common as an internal measurement.

Obviously, the external size will depend on thickness of timber used, and when visiting Chinese apiaries around Beijing in 1985, I remember thinking that their Langstroths seemed larger, but this proved to be because of thicker walls (over an inch thick, in some cases). The internal measurements were standard, as were the frames.

As already mentioned, the great discovery for which Langstroth will always be remembered is that bees respect a space of about $\frac{1}{4}$ inch around their combs, using such a space as a corridor for access. He was the first to make and use frames hanging by their lugs from rebates cut into the hive walls, so that all around, sides, top and bottom, there was this free space. In this sense, every frame made for the last one hundred and forty years has been and is a Langstroth frame, though the name is usually applied only to those frames specifically made to fit in the Langstroth rectangular hive. Like all really great discoveries and inventions, it seems so simple once it has been accepted, and the trouble over his patent rights really arose when his bee-space principle was applied to frames varying slightly from his in size.

At various times claims have been made that others had previously invented the bee space. The evidence is that although suspended frames were described by Major Munn (Britain) in 1834, by Prokopoertel (Holland) in 1841, by Dzierzon (Silesia) in 1845, by Debeauvoys (France) and others later, all these frames had to be cut or forcibly separated from hive walls in order to be removed. In the case of Dzierzon this was not difficult as he used the German magazine type hive with rear access.

In the third edition of his 'Guide de l'Apiculteur' 1851, Debeauvoys recommended the use of rectangular frames having 6 mm clearance from side walls, but only *in order to reduce wax moth trouble*.

A highly respected French beekeeper, M. Philippe Baldensperger of Nice, for many years editor of a bee journal published by the 'Société des Alpes-Maritimes', went deeply into the question of who invented the frame plus bee-space and wrote as follows: 'The Debeauvoys hive was at one time in favour but was found to be too complicated and abandoned.' A Frenchman named Charles Dadant living in Illinois, U.S.A. was the first to publicize Langstroth's invention in France, leading to the adoption of the Dadant hive as a variant of the original Langstroth hive. That great directeur of 'La Gazette Apicole', M. Alphandéry, wrote in 1931: '—Langstroth, in my opinion, was the true creator of the modern hive. After him other hives, the Dadant, the Dadant-Blatt, the Layens and others were all derived from his invention' (p. 113 "Traité Complet d'Apiculture", edition Berger-Llevrault, Paris, 1931'.) Having studied all the available evidence, I am convinced that L. L. Langstroth was indeed the first to build and use a practicable, moveable frame hive with hanging frames plus bee space.

Simple ideas are hard to patent and people tend to say that it is so obvious that 'anyone could have thought of that', even though

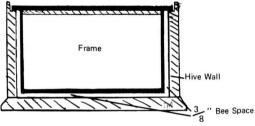

A Langstroth frame

for centuries before 1851, no-one did! Had patent laws been in force at the time, could someone have patented the wheel? Or the use of fire at cave entrances to keep away wild animals? So it was that the great man died in poverty, with subscriptions raised in America, Canada and Britain to sustain him. We may be proud that in Britain the founder and first editor of 'B.B.J.' (C. N. Abbott) and a former President of the B.B.K.A. (T. W. Cowan) took the lead in this (1879), followed by Canada in 1883.

CHAPTER TEN

REV. DR JOHN DZIERZON 1811–1906

Born at Lowkowitz, a small village near Kreuzburg in Silesia, John Dzierzon* was familiar with bees from his earliest childhood. His father was a small farmer who kept hives and encouraged his son's interest in them. A child of exceptional ability, he soon outgrew the

*Publisher's note. He was also known as Jan or Johann (*see* British Bee Books, 1979)

resources of his village school and attended the town school of Pitschen, about a mile away. Shortly after his eleventh birthday he studied in Breslau, first at school and then at University, where he was consistently first in the class and graduated with distinction in 1833. He himself said that he chose a career in the church in order to have more time with his bees, and in 1834 became chaplain at Schalkowitz for the final year of study before his appointment as a Catholic priest to the curacy of Carlsmarkt, a village in Silesia where he lived for the next fifty years. Dzierzon finally returned to his birthplace in 1884 and lived with his nephew for a time before setting up by himself next door on a three acre site with some 200 hives and mating nuclei. In a letter to a bee journal in August 1885, he expressed his deep content and spoke of living in 'an earthly paradise'.

His name will always be associated with parthenogenesis, or virgin birth as with drones. It had been thought that all creatures had to have both a father and a mother, and when Dzierzon first proclaimed in 1846 that drones originated from unfertilized eggs, he faced scorn and ridicule. However, within two years, Professor Theodor von Siebold of the University of Munich published his findings on the dissection of bee eggs under a microscope, which settled the argument. Out of a total of 52 eggs from worker cells, von Siebold found 34 which still had seminal filaments both inside and outside the egg; in several cases they were still moving, as entire sperms. Out of 27 eggs from drone cells, not a single filament of semen could be found either inside or outside, and the world accepted that drones arose from unfertilized eggs.

He was probably the first beekeeper consistently to use small nucleus hives for queen rearing, and also to set up a business producing queens rather than honey and wax. Dzierzon also pioneered queen bee importation into Germany, when he brought a hive of yellow Italian bees from Mira (near Venice) to Silesia via Trieste and Vienna. They arrived safely on 12 February 1853, and from them later that year he reared 27 pure Italian stocks.

He commented on their gentle disposition and extraordinary activity, and mentioned their collection of pollen early in March when his black German bees were scarcely flying at all. He also praised their large honey yields, efficient defence against robbers and the bright colour of the queens, enabling them to be found 'four times more easily than black queens, which tended to hide in crevices'. On the scientific side, Dzierzon noted the striking change of colour of the progeny when black bees were requeened with a yellow Italian queen. This confirmed his opinion that worker bees in summer seldom lived longer than six weeks, but could live more than six months over winter. Also that it was the reigning queen that left the hive with the first swarm, and that pure Italian drones were produced by first generation queens mated by black drones. This followed naturally from his own explanation of parthenogenesis.

Although it has been suggested that Dzierzon and Berlepsch operated moveable frame hives before Langstroth, a closer analysis shows that the expression 'moveable frame' was used in respect of combs fastened just to a top-bar. What Dzierzon did introduce was the German magazine or side-loading hive, which enabled relatively easy access for cutting away the combs fastened to hive sides. To this day this type of hive is common, especially in bee houses, in Germany and nowhere else. In and around Carlsmarkt he kept up to 400 hives, in several apiaries.

On hive design in general, Dzierzon commented that winter losses were often due to dysentery arising from damp, and advocated the use of a thick quilt of jute (old carpet), which both absorbed and allowed water to evaporate; he found that better hive ventilation also stopped damp.

Like Brother Adam a century later, Dzierzon tried various races of bees and commented that the original black bee was so bad-tempered that often the police had to take action when neighbours were stung by them, whereas both Italian and Carniolan bees were remarkably gentle and easy to handle. Italian bees were the better gatherers and after twenty-five years of experience he preferred them to all others, especially the Ligurian bees from Northern Italy. Egyptian bees were pronounced useless, breeding all the time and wintering badly. Cyprian bees had some good points but had shorter wings and poorer flying ability.

Dzierzon wrote his first book 'Theory and Practice of Beekeeping' in 1848 and from 1854–56 published a monthly beekeeping journal 'The Bee-master of Silesia'. From 1850 onwards, he contributed many articles to 'Bienenzeitung', many of which were translated and reprinted in journals world-wide, including our own 'British Bee Journal'. He produced his main book 'Rational Beekeeping' in 1878; this was translated into English and published by C. N. Abbott in 1882.

In his later years he received many awards and distinctions, Diplomas of Honour from learned societies and an honorary Doctorate from Munich University; many international awards including Orders of Chivalry from the Emperor of Russia and the King of Sweden, as well as from several other countries. Beekeepers from all over the world visited him at his home for many years, and spoke of the warm welcome always given to them.

CHAPTER ELEVEN

THOMAS WHITE WOODBURY 1818–1870

This great beekeeper came to Devon from London at the age of 14 when his father took over as proprietor of the 'Exeter and Plymouth Gazette'. He worked as a journalist in Exeter and Edgbaston, but retired early for health reasons and came back to live in the Mount Radford area, near Exeter, in 1850. From this date until his death on 26 July 1870, he dedicated himself to beekeeping. He wrote regularly for the 'Cottage Gardener' and the 'Gardeners' Chronicle'. When the 'Journal of Horticulture' started publication in 1861 he wrote also for that, and occasionally for 'The Times' under the pen-name of 'A Devonshire Bee-keeper'.

So far as I can trace, he wrote no book, although his published articles would have filled one very adequately. He was well known world-wide during his lifetime, and corresponded with Charles Darwin (who also wrote for 'The Gardeners' Chronicle'), L. L.

Langstroth and others. The twenty years of Woodbury's dedication to bees were years of great change, more so than in any previous period of one hundred years in my opinion.

Moveable Frame Hive

Nowadays when every beginner starts off with a wooden hive plus moveable frames arranged so as to leave a bee-space between them and the walls, it all looks so simple, but Woodbury was born in an age when most bees were kept in straw skeps. There were indeed some square hives, but these were really 'wooden skeps' with fixed combs, however ingenious the arrangement of the various boxes may have been.

The great leap forward was the use of moveable frames, which gave rise to a host of possible management techniques, apart from the convenience of examining each comb at will. It was in 1860 that Woodbury developed the 10-frame hive for which he is chiefly remembered. Basically this was a square hive made of inch thick pine having inside measurements of $14\frac{1}{2} \times 14\frac{1}{2} \times 9$ inches ($368 \times 368 \times 187$ mm). The frames had short lugs resting in rebates cut into opposing walls, leaving a top bee space of $\frac{3}{8}$ inch, and a generous space under. This gave a total comb area of 942 square inches (6,077 square centimetres), rather less than that in a single National brood box taking 11 frames, comb area 1,169 square inches (7,542 square centimetres). This hive was in use for the next twenty years or more.

Essentially the Woodbury hive was very similar to the Smith hive, but slightly smaller in brood capacity; it led directly to the national type of brood box in such general use today. All the essentials were there, moveable frames, a beespace to prevent the frames becoming waxed or propolized to the sides and a simple forerunner of the queen excluder. Woodbury even kept his hives in pairs on '. . . rails 2 inches square placed 12 inches apart nailed to posts driven into the ground to give 6 inches clearance . . .'

Perhaps because he was preoccupied with the need to keep his frames from swinging when the hives were moved, Woodbury at first put notched bars on his floors into which the frame slotted, but these were omitted from later versions. Although Woodbury himself used wooden hives the beekeeping public in the 1860s felt that nothing could be so good for bees as straw, and since the customer is always right, Geo. Neighbour & Sons in 1862, started making a Woodbury hive with straw sides, using for the purpose a machine modelled on one exhibited in the Austrian Department of the 1862 International Exhibition. From various accounts it seems likely that more of this type of hive were made than of the wooden one preferred by Woodbury.

Ligurian Mountain Bees

In 1859 Woodbury imported a yellow Ligurian queen from Mr Hermann in Switzerland. She arrived by train on 3 August in a rough deal box with about a thousand worker bees. Woodbury had prepared an 8-bar hive, including four frames of honey and pollen plus one empty comb, and he gently shook the newcomers into this. Then he took a skep of local black bees weighing $34\frac{1}{2}$ pounds and shook them out in clusters on four cloths spread out on the grass; helped by his friend Mr Fox. He found and took out the queen, before placing the hive with Ligurian queen and bees over the shaken bees. Alas they fought, and in the morning there were many dead bees, but he hoped for the best. By 17 August, great loads of pollen were going in, and he knew that the first queen from outside Britain had been introduced. When he wrote about this in the 'Cottage Gardener' he had letters from all over the country asking for stocks from this queen for next year, so at once he telegraphed for two more queens (one for Mr Fox) and they arrived on 27 August having been four days on the way. Although most of the bees were dead, each package had their queen still living, and each queen was successfully introduced to a colony. In response to a further telegram two more queens arrived on 10 September, but when Woodbury asked for more still, Mr Hermann told him it was too late in the year.

Over these momentous weeks Woodbury evolved his technique of introducing queens via a small cage with a perforated zinc slide, which he opened after a couple of days. In response to many requests, Woodbury agreed to raise and mate Ligurian queens from his apiary, moving away all other stocks from his garden, thinking that with no rival hives nearer than one and a half miles, he could maintain the pure strain! He promised to provide queens at half a guinea each, orders to be dealt with in strict rotation. Alas the summer in 1860 turned out to be wretched, and with ill-health beginning to trouble him, only one Ligurian-mated queen was produced; this went to a correspondent in Renfrew, Scotland. The wettest summer for many years was followed by the most severe winter, and Woodbury noted with pleasure that the tough, yellow Alpine bees survived better than the old English blacks, and he records them foraging for pollen on one day in January when the temperature rose briefly to 40°F. The Scottish bees also survived (despite a Renfrew temperature of 33 degree of frost (-1°F) on 24 December 1860). Issues of 'Journal of Horticulture' over the next few years were full of evidence of the yellow bee's superiority, recording bigger yields of honey, earlier spring build-up, working at lower temperatures and being much easier to handle. This introduction of new blood by Woodbury was a great advance for British beekeeping, and although it is very easy to sentimentalize about the vanished British black bees, the beekeepers of the 1870s were unanimous in preferring the Ligurians. Here I quote Mr T. W. Cowan, Editor of 'British Bee Journal' and Chairman of the British Beekeepers' Association, who said in 1893: 'Much prejudice existed against Ligurian bees at first, but their superiority over the common black bees is now almost universally admitted. This introduction has done much to improve our race of black bees by introducing new blood.'

Another great achievement in 1862 was the successful export of four stocks of Ligurian bees to Australia. Woodbury himself packed them (on behalf of Geo. Neighbour & Sons) and they sailed on 25 September in the steamship 'Alhambra', arriving in Melbourne on 12 December. 'They have since multiplied' said a newspaper report, 'the climate and pasturage of Australia greatly favouring the increase of this superior variety of bee.'

Woodbury died quite suddenly in Exeter at the early age of 52, leaving a widow and two daughters. His work is much more fully covered in '1000 Years of Devon Bee-keeping' published by Devon B.K.A. in 1975 to celebrate their centenary.

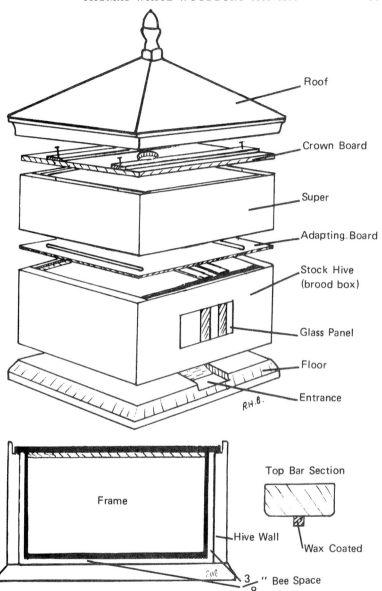

Roof

Crown Board

Super

Adapting Board

Stock Hive
(brood box)

Glass Panel

Floor

Entrance

R.H.B.

Top Bar Section

Frame

Hive Wall

Wax Coated

$\frac{3}{8}$ " Bee Space

The Woodbury Hive 1860
Drawn from illustrations published by Geo. Neighbour & Sons, 1865

CHAPTER TWELVE

CHARLES NASH ABBOTT
1830–1894

Deservedly famous as the founder of the 'British Bee Journal', Abbott served as its first editor (and arguably the best) from 1873–1882. He went on to develop the Abbott Standard Hive and also played a leading role in the formulation and adoption of the British Standard Frame in 1882. The dimensions were set at $14 \times 8\frac{1}{2}$ inches (external) with a top bar 17 inches long, thus having the characteristic 'long lugs'. It remains the same today, and enabled basic designs of honey extractors as well as hives to be stabilized.

Abbott first started with bees as a boy of twelve when he took a swarm which arrived on a tree in the family garden. Leaving school in 1844 he served an apprenticeship of six years as a butcher and was then set up in business himself. He played cricket at Lords for the Master Butchers' XI v. Licensed Victuallers, and also became a Colour Sergeant in the Volunteers (1867), set up rather like the Territorial Army today. He was at this time a champion rifle shot.

After inheriting his father's estate, he sold the butchers business and with Doctor Coster as Medical Officer, administered a large school for poor children. Coster was already an acknowledged authority on bees and bee-keeping, and Abbott learned much from him. In 1870 he began to write bee articles for the 'Journal of Horticulture', the 'English Mechanic' and the 'Middlesex County Times', and rapidly acquired the expertise so evident in his editorship of the 'B.B.J.' He was the driving force behind the first Crystal Palace Honey Show (September 1874), which later became the 'National Honey Show' so popular today.

The actual foundation of the 'B.B.J.' involved a great deal of very hard work and continued effort, with little encouragement in the early stages. On the strength of just sixty subscribers, 3,000 copies of the very first issue were printed in May 1873 and over 2,500 distributed free of charge. In June, 1,500 copies were sent free of charge to clergymen and in July 500 copies to agriculturalists; even so, the regular subscription list was barely 200. After this the journal caught on and began to attract writers and beekeepers over the English-speaking world. Reading the early issues today, one hundred and twenty years later, one is struck by the faithful attention to detail and the conscientious way all individual queries were answered. In 1881 he and W. Carr spent four weeks on a lecture tour of Ireland.

His early photographs show a slim, powerfully-built young man, but in later years he developed the 'full figure' so admired by prosperous Victorians.

His father was a builder, carpenter and undertaker in Hanwell, with a family business going back to 1760. While engaged on contract work with the G.W.R. his father saved the life of the great engineer I. K. Brunel, and was almost knocked over by the same trains (two were passing at that time and Brunel only noticed one).

His descendants have also made contributions to beekeeping and his grandson Charles Pryce Abbott was President of the Middlesex County B.K.A. from 1946–1951, also Chairman of the Central Association and for five years Treasurer of the Bee Research Association. In 1962 he was awarded the M.B.E. for his work with B.D.I. (Bee Disease Insurance) scheme.

CHAPTER THIRTEEN

FIVE INVENTORS

Johannes Mehring (Germany)—Wax Foundation 1857

He was the first to produce foundation made from pure beeswax, cast in a metal mould to give hexagonal imprints on both sides.

There were earlier experimentalists, who dipped glass sheets or wetted wooden boards in melted beeswax and peeled off the smooth wax sheets for the bees to work. Also Kretchmer in 1842 (Germany) had produced waxed cloth rolled out stiff and flat, but these were not always accepted by the bees, which would often ignore them and build thin natural combs alongside.

In April 1875, the Editor of 'B.B.J.' wrote, 'Under no circumstances is it necessary or safe to use impressed wax sheets of a greater depth than $1\frac{1}{2}$ inches in supers or stock hives.' This comment related to the advertisement in that journal of 'a pair of plates 6×2 inches for five shillings—long and deep enough for any super'. It was soon outdated when wire reinforced foundation became available.

In 1876 the firm of A. I. Root in the U.S.A. began to manufacture wax foundation on a large scale, using cylindrical metal rollers to form the hexagonal cell bases. A final improvement was the production by Mr E. B. Weed (U.S.A. 1895) of foundation having cells with raised edges, more easily worked by the bees.

Major Franz von Hruschka (Austria)—Honey Extractor 1865

This was invented by accident. He cut out a fine new comb of honey (unsealed), put it on a plate in a basket and told his young son to take it to mother. On the way from hive to home the bees were worrying the boy, so he swung the basket round and round at head level. His mother was surprised to see a plate of pure liquid honey and a comb with the upper side full and the lower side empty. When father came home later on, he was shown this and understood the principle at once. Next day, he made a crude 'honey slinger' which he used to extract several pounds of honey. This was written about in gardening journals and in 1869, Mr. A. I. Root in the U.S.A. designed a machine with a crank handle and gears giving a 3 : 1 increase in revolutions. A correspondent in the very first issue of the 'British Bee Journal' (May 1873) mentioned this, and Mr C. N. Abbott (Editor) commented that he had ordered one at a cost of fifteen U.S. dollars (then about £3). Mr Abbott also wrote of a home-made 'slinger', a tin dish with a wire cover and strings from each corner, to be whirled around from a stick. Later Thomas Cowan in England designed and made several improved machines, including one which reversed the combs automatically (1875). At first, these were all tangential, but Cowan also built a radial model. Press reports at the time record sales of American extractors in Britain and also of Cowan's models in America. However, there is no doubt as to the real inventor and in 1874, Major Hruschka was awarded a medal in Italy, purchased by public subscription from beekeepers everywhere.

Abbé Collin (France)—Queen Excluder 1865

The first queen excluder was made of thin sheet iron drilled with round holes having a diameter of $\frac{3}{16}$ inch (4.76 mm). This allowed worker bees to pass through, except where the drill had burred the edges, but also quite often the queen also. When a smaller hole was used, many worker bees were stuck in the openings. After a time it was realized in France that this difficulty did not occur if oval or oblong slots were used. A big advance was made when zinc came into use instead of iron; the softer metal was more readily polished to remove the rough edges. For many years both long slot and short slot zinc excluders have been in use, but the latter are more generally approved, as they are stronger and have a longer life.

For some years there were reports of disasters arising from blocked holes causing panic and meltdown of combs through lack of ventilation, and this caused many beekeepers in Britain to be prejudiced against the use of any queen excluder. By 1878 the problem was more generally understood, namely that although the abdomen of a worker was approximately the same diameter as the thorax of a queen, the former was flexible and could be squeezed through an oval slot, whereas the queen's thorax was rigid. For many years now the accepted width of slots in zinc excluders has been 0.167 inch (4.24 mm) but slightly less for wire excluders 0.163 inch (4.14 mm). The Abbé Collin who invented the excluder was the author of 'Le guide du propriétaire d'abeilles' (1856).

Mr T. F. Bingham (U.S.A.)—Improved Smoker 1877

Mankind has used smoke to subdue or calm honeybees for thousands of years, long before they were kept in hives. A favourite method in Africa was to blow smoke from a smouldering piece of cow dung held in the hand while robbing a wild colony in a tree. Dried elephant dung is even better, having a higher fibre content, and I remember bringing back a sack of 'gargantuan bounty' as Darwin called it, to use in my own modern smoker, from a family holiday off the beaten track. Why not contact your local zoo? Various primitive containers were devised, some with bellows attached, but the great step forward was made by Bingham, who invented the short gap between smoke box and air jet tube coming from the bellows. This allows a slow uptake of air to keep the fuel smouldering without continually working the bellows, so that a beekeeper can keep the smoker going slowly while driving from one apiary to another, and quickly coax it back into smoke production in a few puffs.

Moses Quinby did most of the early work on the smoker, but it was Bingham who patented it.

Mr E. C. Porter (U.S.A.)—Bee Escape 1891

All beekeepers face the problem of how to take off supers or boxes of honey without at the same time taking with them thousands of bees. Over a hundred years ago, Porter invented the device with two pairs of very thin, closely spaced, springy metal. This allows bees to squeeze through quite easily, but not to return. Rejoining the queen below is the motivating force for the bees. The typical Porter escape fits neatly into the oval feeder slot in a standard crownboard, so that when the supers are removed twenty-four to forty-eight hours later, the crownboard (with escapes removed) is already in the correct position for winter feeding of syrup, if needed. The great advantage in a garden (with neighbours) is that supers of honey can then be lifted off quickly without the bees even noticing. Occasionally, a pair of springs may be jammed by a drone in the wrong box, so that two escapes are better (and faster) than one. Before this invention the bees were either 'bumped' off (which can break combs) or brushed off with a goose wing or bee brush. More modern methods range from motor-driven bee blowers to cloths impregnated with a repellent such as benzaldehyde; these are only effective in hot weather and in my experience, work better in Queensland and North Island, New Zealand, than in the U.K. Escapes with gauze and plastic tunnels, can now also be obtained.

CHAPTER FOURTEEN

WILLIAM BROUGHTON CARR 1836–1909

Remembered mainly because of the W.B.C. hive named after him, Carr was apprenticed to a copperplate engraver and remained in this business in Liverpool for twenty-six years; demanding meticulous attention to detail, this early training probably formed some of the habits which made him such a great bee-master.

By an extraordinary co-incidence another talented bee-keeper also named William Carr and of about the same age, lived and worked in the same general area (Chester/Manchester) over the same period, but died in 1903. When writing for 'The British Beekeeping Journal', our subject signed himself W. Broughton Carr, Higher Bebington, Cheshire whereas his 'namesake' signed himself William Carr, Newton Heath, Nr. Manchester. The two addresses are just over 30 miles apart, more than enough to keep their bees from contact but close enough to cause some confusion among beekeepers over 100 years later. On 1 Aug 1874 both these beekeepers wrote at some length in the B.B.J. William Broughton Carr exhorting beekeepers to exhibit at the forthcoming Crystal Palace honey show, and William Carr explaining the differing ways in which worker bees react to mated and virgin queens. By yet another odd coincidence, a much more impressive letter from Thos. Wm. Cowan of Horsham (the subject of the next chapter) was sandwiched between letters from the two Williams!

William Carr continued to write frequently for the BBJ, while William Broughton Carr wrote for, and was in charge of the 'Beekeepers' Record' from its first issue in 1882, the year in which he helped to form the Lancashire and Cheshire Beekeepers' Association. However, Broughton joined the BBJ staff in 1890 and later became joint editor with T. W. Cowan until his death in 1909. He was also a member of the Council of the B.B.K.A. for many years, and he it was who designed the frame-spacers stamped out of thin template and folded into clip-on metal ends. May he be forgiven! I cannot trace any book written by W. B. Carr, but Col. Walker's Library list quotes details of a 9 × 6 inch book of 478 pages, attributed to William Carr of Newton Heath Apiary, near Manchester. I have tried to cover the background of the 'other William' in the hope that readers of this book will not fall into the trap that I so nearly did, of assuming that William Carr was just a shortened form of William Broughton Carr.

The White W.B.C. Hive

Bearing his initials and his passport to beekeeping immortality, this rapidly became the most common hive in use in Britain from about 1890. It is still being made and used today, but for many years now has been falling out of favour for several reasons, principally expense and awkwardness in moving (as for pollination, heather-honey, etc.). To the general public it still, like a straw skep, remains the symbol of bee-hiving generally; many people prefer to have a W.B.C. on their front lawn, but Nationals in their main apiary. The outer telescopic lift enclosing bee boxes of lighter construction ensures a drier hive, and some experienced beekeepers in the wetter areas still prefer this arrangement. It also gives complete protection against woodpeckers. On the other hand, the beneficial warming-up of spring sunshine is less effective in a double-walled hive. Perhaps the very popularity of the hive, resulting in slight variations arising from different manufacturers (and home-made versions) has itself produced the exasperating lack of standardization, when components acquired from different sources do not fit one upon another. The fact that supers rest upon the actual lugs of frames in each other make them difficult to separate in a good year, and the extra labour of removing outer lifts before having access to the bee boxes, add to their awkwardness; likewise, the difficulty of carrying out such standard procedures on a Demaree or a Snelgrove. On the other hand, some outer lifts are large enough to enclose a standard National hive, should one wish to do so. So many W.B.C. hives were made at a time when British quality had a well-deserved reputation, that these hives will survive well past the year 2000, and a good solid outer lift can be made into a solar wax extractor, a very strong container of garden produce and used in many other ways.

Despite the adverse comments made, it is only fair to say that two highly regarded commercial beekeepers did very well with about five hundred W.B.C. hives for many years; that great character Tom Bradford and also the Firkin family.

It is also only fair to point out that the W.B.C. hive uses normal British Standard frames, identical with those used in the British National hive, but of course having only ten frames in the brood chamber instead of eleven.

The Man Himself

His contemporaries wrote of him as a wonderful manipulator of bees, with few indeed equalling his practical ability; he was in great demand as a demonstrator all over Britain. In his latter years he suffered from bronchial asthma and died on 11 February 1909, leaving four sons and four daughters. He was buried at Lewisham Cemetery, Ladywell, in South East London.

CHAPTER FIFTEEN

THOMAS WILLIAM COWAN
1840–1926

What an outstanding record of service to British beekeeping! Cowan was Hon. Chairman of the B.B.K.A. in 1874 and holding that office continually for 48 years, when he was unanimously elected President; Proprietor and Editor of the 'British Bee Journal' from 1887 until his death over forty years later (with J. Herrod-Hempsall as assistant latterly); Chairman of the Board of Examiners which initiated beekeeping examinations at three levels, viz. elementary, intermediate and advanced.

His Books

He wrote books covering the whole range of bees and beekeeping. Outstanding here was his 'British Bee-keeping Guide Book', first published in 1881, twenty-fourth and final edition in 1924, total production 100,000 copies, and in addition translated into seven foreign languages. His 'Honey Bee—Natural History, Anatomy and Physiology' was the standard scientific work from 1890 until 1910, when Snodgrass and Zander published their books. Also his 'Wax Craft' published in 1908 and remaining the only British book on beeswax until 1981.*

His Life

Born in St Petersburg, where his father was an engineer in the Russian government service, Cowan was educated in Russia and later trained as an engineer at the London School of Mines. He took over the family business (Kent Iron Works) from his father in 1862. An early motorist, he was one of those pioneers who, in Victorian days, drove a steam car through the streets of London at the maximum permitted speed of four m.p.h. preceded by a man on foot carrying a red flag.

As fluent in Russian as in English, Cowan also spoke German, French and Dutch, frequently travelling abroad; in fact, he lived in France for most of 1884 on account of his wife's illness, and commuted to Britain for work. As the owner of a thriving family business, he had no financial problems and subsidized the 'British Bee Journal' until it paid for itself, eventually producing it as the

* *Publisher's Note* When Ron Brown's 'Beeswax' was published.

THE
Feminine Monarchie :

OR

THE HISTORIE
OF BEES.

SHEWING

Their admirable Nature, and Properties,
Their Generation, and Colonies,
Their Gouernment, Loyaltie, Art, Induſtrie,
Enemies, Warres, Magnanimitie, &c.

TOGETHER

With the right ordering of them from time to
time : And the ſweet profit ariſing thereof.

Written out of Experience
By
CHARLES BVTLER. *Magd:*

Plaut: in Trucul: Act: 2. Sc. 6.
Pluris eſt oculatus teſtis unus, quam auriti decem.

LONDON,
Printed by IOHN HAVILAND for *Roger Iackſon,*
and are to be ſold at his Shop in Fleetſtreet, ouer
againſt the Conduit. 1. 6 2 3.

*Title page of Charles Butler's
"The Feminine Monarchie", 1623*

Revd. L.L. Langstroth

François Huber

Dr. J. Dzeirzon

C.N. Abbott as a young man

W. Broughton Carr

Yours sincerely
W. Herrod-Hempsal

W. Herrod-Hemps

T. W. Woodbury, 1870

Revd. J. Digges

T.W. Cowan

R.O.B. Manley

Yours very truly,
L. E. Snelgrove.

L. Snelgrove

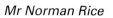
Mr Norman Rice

Brother Adam at his queen-mating apiary

Miss Annie D. Betts, B.Sc.

Rothamsted E.S. Bee department staff in 1957. From left to right standing: James Simpson, Norman Ellement, David Lee, Bill Stevens Anthony Griffin, Fred Woodstock, Ron Welch, Peter Tomkins; seated Valerie Bramley, Leslie Bailey, John Free, Colin Butler, Lorna Stevens Inge Riedel, Yvette Spencer-Booth.

only weekly bee journal in the world (which it still was when I started beekeeping in 1950).

Cowan moved to Horsham in 1870 and in 1878 built a mansion in about fifty acres at Compton's Lea. In his later years he lived for a time in California, where a son had a fruit farm, and on his return moved to Upcott House, Bishops Hull near Taunton; here he stayed for several years before moving to Sutherland House, Clevedon in 1918. On 17 May 1926 he fell from a step ladder while reaching for a book in his library and died of internal injuries six days later.

His Beekeeping

Cowan started in 1864, after reading Woodbury's articles in the 'Journal of Horticulture'. After some correspondence with Woodbury in Exeter, he bought a number of his new frame hives and set up an apiary of fifteen identical ones, also a Stewarton and some skeps. Later he established nearly thirty Woodburys in lofts over the stables, but came to the conclusion that bees did best in the open air. All his life he preferred to do without spacers, using 'deftness of feel and an educated eye' when arranging frames in a hive. As a disciple of Woodbury, he used Ligurian or Italian bees throughout his career and had a poor opinion of the Old English black bees, used by cottagers in skeps.

With his fifty acres and ample private means, he was able to grow significant areas of plants just for bees. This included an acre of buckwheat, half an acre of mustard and several large patches of catmint, his favourite bee forage. He also had his own museum of hives and beekeeping apparatus, including an ancient Hruschka honey-slinger. Likewise he had a private geological museum.

Despite his money, Cowan was definitely a 'hands-on beekeeper', unlike wealthy contemporaries who employed beekeepers and watched from a distance. His books are full of practical advice, for example, the importance of rearing and using young queens to get large honey yields. Also the use of carbolic acid (four tablespoons to the quart) to impregnate driving or clearer cloths, or to moisten a goose wing to persuade bees to enter a hive of skep.

After years of discussion, a committee of the B.B.K.A. chaired by Cowan agreed unanimously on 16 March 1882 to adopt the Standard British Frame, with a comb area of $13\frac{1}{2} \times 8$ inches (inside frame), $14 \times 8\frac{1}{2}$ inches outside measurement. This was virtually identical to the Woodbury frame at that time used by many beekeepers (excluding skeppists).

Contemporary records are full of his success at the Crystal Palace and other honey shows. In one year he took First Prize in several categories, also First Prize and a silver medal for an improved automatic reversing extractor. The value of the prizes in those days made them really worthwhile. A First of £3 in 1876 would have paid the wage of a farm labourer for three months! At the very first Crystal Palace Show he exhibited a total of over 700 pounds of honey, from twelve Woodbury hives, headed by Ligurian queens (as were all his stocks).

In an address to the annual B.B.K.A. Congress in 1908, Cowan reported that 63,000 beekeepers in Britain kept bees in wooden frame hives, as well as an unknown number still using straw skeps. With many examples of over 100 pounds of honey per hive, this must have been a golden age for British beekeeping, well before the introduction of insecticides and industrial farming techniques.

A full list of his published papers and lectures, visits and honorary awards would cover too much space, but shining through all reports, one gains the impression of a man of very great talent, yet with a quiet and unassuming manner, always ready with help and advice, above all, a true Christian gentleman. He left his library of bee books (comparable to that of Lt. Col. Walker) to the B.B.K.A. Until very recently, it was conveniently and readily available at the Ministry of Agriculture, Whitehall Place, London. Alas, when I applied to visit it again recently, I was told that it had been moved to Luddington; logical perhaps, but more difficult for most of us.*

* Publisher's note. The library was sold by B.B.K.A. to M.A.F.F. several years ago.

The Rev. Charles Butler (1559–1647) has been called 'the father of British bee-keepers'. Perhaps we should call him 'grandfather' and award paternity to Cowan.

CHAPTER SIXTEEN

REV. J. R. G. DIGGES 1857–1933

Although no particular discovery or invention has been linked to his name, Joseph Digges will always be remembered as a great beekeeper who wrote with understanding and authority. He shared his own knowledge with beekeepers all over the British Isles via his monthly magazines 'The Irish Bee Journal' and the 'Bee-keepers' Gazette', and of course, his book 'The Practical Bee Guide'.

Editor

In No. 1, Vol. 1 of May 1901, 'The Irish Bee Journal' (price one penny) gave some excellent advice, worth quoting today: 'Woe to the man who has allowed the Spring to pass and May to find him unprepared. To him belong the hurried scramble, the work half done, the disordered apiary and neglected hives, the famishing bees in empty feeders—which not enriches him and makes them poor indeed.' So popular did this journal become that from 1911 it was also published (with a different cover) as the 'Bee-keepers' Gazette', adopted by twenty-seven associations in Scotland and England as their official organ, carrying their local association news, reports of honey shows, letters to the Editor, and so on. So dominating was his personality and knowledge of beekeeping that when he died suddenly, no-one could be found to replace him, and even after some weeks only one more issue was ever published. For the next fourteen years, no regular monthly journal appeared, until January 1947, when 'The Irish Bee-keeper, An Beachaire' took over and continues today.

Author

His 'Practical Bee Guide' ran to seven editions during his lifetime and another nine after his death, to a total of over 76,000 copies. No other bee book of comparable size or scope has gone to so many editions. (T. W. Cowan's 'British Bee-keeping Guide Book' ran to twenty-five editions, but was a much slimmer production).

Three years after Digges' death, R. O. B. Manley revised the book and made a few changes to bring the eighth edition up-to-date; Miss A. D. Betts also helped in this, and the sixteenth edition was published in 1950. Obviously written before the invention of electron microscopes, and before the Rothamsted work on queen substance, pheromones and bee virus diseases, it could with advantage, be revised again. It remains a great book, extremely well illustrated and with well-organized material, worthy of a place in any beekeeper's library.

Judged as a literary work, it is easily the best of the general guides to beekeeping ever published in the British Isles.

The Man Himself

An ordained Minister of the Church of Ireland for fifty years, Joseph Digges was said by his parishioners to be strict, even severe at times, but respected as a man of great ability and influence. Always deeply interested in bees, he encouraged others to keep them. As a strong character with very definite ideas of his own, he had problems with the Irish Bee-keepers' Association, which in 1903 actually dismissed him from their Executive Committee and also from the Editorship of the 'Irish Bee Journal', founded and run by him since May 1901. However, in the event, it was the Committee which resigned, leaving Digges in complete control. After his death, R. O. B. Manley wrote, 'At Clooncahir a chair stands empty and a once-active pen lies still, after 32 years of continuous editorship. Never again shall we read his bright editorials, or enjoy the humour of his gems, or travel with him on his continental bee holidays'. Like the Rev. L. L. Langstroth, he also died suddenly, while taking a service in the church which he had served so many years as rector.

CHAPTER SEVENTEEN

THE HERROD-HEMPSALL BROTHERS JOSEPH 1870–1958, WILLIAM 1873–1951

Early Years

Both were born and brought up in Sutton-on-Trent, Nottinghamshire, a village of under a thousand population, and left the village school when aged thirteen years. Joseph was apprenticed to a local carpenter, William worked for sixpence a day as a garden boy. While still at school they used to watch bees in an apiary of skeps nearby, thrilled to see swarms taken and hived; horrified to see colonies killed over sulphur pits at the end of summer. In 1888 they borrowed a copy of 'British Bee-keepers' Guide Book' (Cowan), made a hive from scrap wood and for a token sum obtained a colony of bees from a local friend, Mr R. Mackender. Alas, in their enthusiasm the boys examined the stock two or three times a day and the poor bees died from exposure and over-manipulation!

That summer they learned the technique of driving bees out of skeps and also over-wintered two skeps of driven bees themselves (on sugar given by mother). During the winter of 1888/89 they made more wooden hives and next summer drove bees from skeps (for other beekeepers) for miles around, selling some bees but keeping enough to build up to 30 stocks before the end of that year.

Rapid Progress

Within ten years William became an acknowledged expert and lectured at Swanley Horticultural College in 1898. From 1909 to 1930 he was Secretary of the B.B.K.A. He was also Joint Editor of the 'British Bee Journal' (with T. W. Cowan) from 1910 and in 1918 accepted the post of Technical Adviser (Beekeeping) to the Ministry of Food. He brought his brother Joseph to London as Office Manager for both the 'B.B.J.' and the 'Bee-keepers' Record' in 1914, and in 1917 Joseph succeeded William as Junior Editor with Cowan, later taking over and holding the post until joined by Cecil Tonsley B.E.M., who became proprietor of the business in 1948.

Links with Devon

In 1923 he lectured on 'Queen Rearing at the Devon A.G.M. in Exeter Guildhall. In 1929 William was at the Devon B.K.A. Annual General Meeting as Guest Speaker, and patiently sat through the business part of the meeting, largely taken up by an endless and fruitless discussion on whether or not to work with the Devon Horticultural Society at a proposed joint county show. Apparently the stumbling block was that the Society offered insufficient space.

Although only a visitor, William jumped up in exasperation and said that Devon beekeepers should back their claim to produce the best honey by an attempt to hold the best honey show. If they would do this, 'he was good for a guinea'. This offer was received with acclamation and broke the deadlock; very soon other offers totalling £21 were received and the meeting decided that the show must be held. Later in the same meeting, members placed on record their disapproval of recent agitation directed against the British Beekeepers' Association (of which William was Secretary!) and stressed that the time was long overdue for individual grievances to be subordinated to the promotion of unity among beekeepers. To round off an unusually good meeting, William then spoke for one and a half hours on spring management and swarm control and emphasized the importance of every beekeeper rearing his own queens. He was roundly cheered and members left saying to each other that this had been the best A.G.M. for many years. Later in the same year came the first residential course for bee-keepers at Seale Hayne Agricultural College, with sixty places at ten shillings a head for a short weekend including full board.

Among the lecturers were William, Brother Adam and Colonel Howorth. What was William's guinea worth, in present day money? It would have paid for two beekeepers to attend the weekend, plus a shilling over for wine. Again, a farm labourer in 1929 was earning thirty shillings a week (£140 now), so a guinea would have equated to around £100 today. A very generous gesture, William; no wonder that you were asked to speak (with Brother Adam) at the next Seale Hayne weekend, expanded to Friday p.m. 18 July—Tuesday midday 22 July 1930, with one hundred places (though now at £1 for full board and residence). I make no apology for reporting these details in full, as they illustrate the dynamic character of the man, and his ability to inspire others to action. Anyone giving such a kick-start to both the Devon Honey Show and our Seale Hayne weekends, must have been a great personality indeed.

Books by William Herrod-Hempsall

The years before the First World War were probably the golden age of honey showmanship, and William's contribution was the classic 'Preparing, Exhibiting and Judging Bee Produce', 168 pages, published by the 'B.B.J.' in 1912 with an expanded 219 page hardback in 1948.

Following this came 'Bee-keeping Simplified for the Cottager and Small-holders' in 1915, 'Bees and their management' in 1916, and Bee-keeping in War-Time' in 1918 (published by 'Country Life'). Later came his 'Anatomy, Physiology and Natural History of the Honey-bee' in 1938 'The Bee-keepers Guide to the Management of Bees in Moveable Comb Hives' 169 pages in 1938 (eighth edition in 1947).

His great and abiding work was 'Bee-keeping, New and Old described with Pen and Camera'. Vol. I of 772 pages published in 1930 and Vol. II of 1070 pages published in 1937.

Nothing comparable has been published, before or since, and

these are now collectors' items, the more valuable because the publisher's plates and frames (especially of Vol. II) were destroyed by German bombs near St Paul's Cathedral during the Second World War.

Up to 1912 they went under the name of 'Herrod' but by 1915 had become 'Herrod-Hempsall F.E.S.'

Brother Joseph

William's elder brother was a good and faithful servant to the craft of beekeeping, but speaking in public was not his strong point. He was sub-editor to Cowan of 'B.B.J.' and 'The Bee-keepers' Record' from 1917, and later became sole Editor, also B.B.K.A. General Secretary from 1930 until the Association was re-constituted in 1944.

Both Joseph and William took more prizes at honey shows than anyone else in the country, over many years. In the opinion of some, Joseph outshone even his illustrious brother as a honey judge. Between them, these two brothers dominated the field of beekeeping in Britain for almost half a century.

Both lived and worked before the invention of A.I., the discovery of pheromones and the electron microscope. But bees have not changed, and the observations and reflections of the 'H-H brothers' were so thorough, so penetrating and so comprehensive that they will always be of very great value to all beekeepers.

CHAPTER EIGHTEEN

LOUIS E. SNELGROVE
1878–1965

As a boy, Snelgrove helped his father to manage eighty stocks around

Warminster, but did not start on his own account until 1900, when he became a member of the Somerset Bee Keepers' Association. He was County Secretary from 1905 to 1912 and finally President from 1926 until his death almost forty years later. For many years he was the official 'visiting expert' and beekeeping lecturer for Somerset County Council. In 1954 he was awarded honorary life membership of the British Beekeeping Association and became its President in 1956.

After training at Culham College, he took his first Degree as an evening student of Bristol University while teaching at a school in Weston-super-Mare, and subsequently went to Queen's University, Belfast, where he took an Honours Degree in Physics and Chemistry in 1907. In 1920 he was awarded an M.Sc. for research on the acarine mite, associated with the Isle of Wight disease. After research into Latin literature relating to beekeeping in Roman times, he was awarded an M.A. in 1922. In 1910 he had been promoted to Headmaster of a large boys' school and four years later he was appointed County Inspector of Schools for Somerset, a position he held until of retiring age.

Snelgrove Board

This world-famous item of bee equipment, invented in 1931, is still in use today. It is essentially a wooden crown board with a gauze screen over the central hole, and with three pairs of wedges in slots about 2 inches (5 cm) wide cut into the extra deep framing on three sides, giving access for bees above and below the board itself. By closing an upper wedge and simultaneously opening the lower one (of the same pair), flying bees returning to that spot are automatically diverted downwards (to the brood box on the floor) to join the reigning queen, instead of going back to the upper brood box. Space will not permit a full description of its use, but briefly, it is for swarm control, by artificially swarming a strong stock so that the queen is in a new box on the hive floor below while the old brood box plus most of the brood and young bees is at the top of the hive, above the Snelgrove board. Flying bees are successively diverted down to the lower box at seven-day intervals until a new queen is ready to mate from the upper box. This maximizes the honey yield from the 'swarm' below, and minimizes the risk of a cast from the old brood box. The operation is an ideal one for a branch apiary meeting once a week.

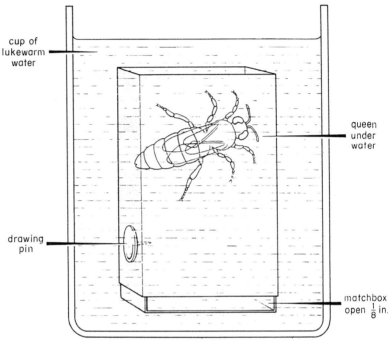

cup of
lukewarm
water

queen
under
water

drawing
pin

matchbox
open $\frac{1}{8}$ in.

Queen Introduction—Snelgrove

His Books

His first publication was a 28-page booklet 'A Method of Re-Queening' (Bristol 1912), followed by his best-known 'Swarming: Its Control and Prevention', first published in 1934, with ten later editions.

'The Introduction of Queen Bees' came out in 1940 and 'Queen Rearing' in 1946. These last two books each ran to two editions, all published privately, the last by his daughter Irene.*

* Publisher's Note. 'Swarming' and 'Queen Rearing' were reprinted by his niece, Barbara Snelgrove, in the nineteen-eighties and are still available.

Apart from his famous board, his best-known innovation is probably the water method of queen introduction. The new queen is isolated for an hour without food in a matchbox, with the drawer very slightly open for ventilation (and a drawing pin through the side to prevent accidental opening or closing). First de-queen the stock concerned and destroy any queen cells present. Use a cup of lukewarm water (at body temperature) and push the matchbox completely under, so that it fills with water, hold it there for six or seven seconds, lift it out so that the water drains away, open and drop the wet queen into the hive between the brood frames. A hungry, humbled queen, wet from her bath, is accepted under almost any circumstances, whether she be mated or not, and the workers lick her and feed her without question, (see illustration).

The Man Himself

I was privileged to meet him at a weekend of beekeeping at Cannington Agricultural College, Somerset, only a few months before his death, and was greatly impressed by his old-fashioned courtesy and his scholarly approach to beekeeping problems. All who knew him spoke of his profound knowledge of bees, his personal integrity and his great service to beekeepers everywhere and to education generally. He was one of Nature's gentlemen.

CHAPTER NINETEEN

ANNIE D. BETTS 1884–1961

From the Rev. Charles Butler to the Rev. Brother Adam, at least half the leading beekeepers in the Western World for the last four hundred years have been ministers of religion. Of the remainder, a large proportion were educated or trained in some branch of applied science, for example, Thomas Cowan in engineering, Christopher

Wren in architecture. Small wonder then, that women have been under-represented. Only in very recent years has it been accepted that women have a contribution to make as engineers or scientists; only while this article was being written did women achieve the right to become ordained ministers in the Church of England.

Against this background, what an unusual lady Miss Annie Betts was, studying science in the last years of Queen Victoria and graduating just after the turn of the century. An engineer as well as a scientist, she worked on aeronautical research projects during the First World War, and rode to work on a motor cycle.

Her first scientific article on bees dealt with '*Pericystis alvei*, a beehive fungus' published in 'The Annals of Botany' and the 'Journal of Economic Biology' in 1912. This work led to the discovery of '*Pericystis apis*' now called '*Ascophaera apis*', or Chalk Brood.

It was thought for many years that the same fungus caused both chalk brood and mouldy pollen, but later work confirmed that the fungus affecting stored pollen (when not covered with honey and wax-capped) was different. The pollen fungus was found to form smaller spore cysts which did not aggregate into spore balls. In 1972 this fungus, known only to affect pollen stored in bee combs, was re-named '*Bettsia alvei*' in honour of the original work carried out some sixty years earlier by Annie Betts. This was seven years before the foundation of the Apis Club and ten years before the establishment of a Bee Research section at Rothamstad Experimental Station. Annie Betts was closely associated with the Apis Club from its formation in 1919, as Editor and President (1930).

By this time she had become an expert on subjects related to bees. She was also a remarkable linguist and not only selected but also translated most of the items from foreign journals which appeared regularly. In 1929 she took over as Manager and Editor of 'The Bee World'; she also played a prominent part in the amalgamation of the Apis Club with the Société des Congrès Internationales d'Apiculture, and with international conferences at various world centres from Quebec in 1924 to Zurich in 1939. The Apis Club finally expanded into the Bee Research Association, and together with the Société des Congrès, into Apimondia in 1950 and

1951. For a few months, 'The Bee World' was also the official organ of Apimondia.

As an independent body, the Apis Club was voluntarily wound up in 1951. Over these years, Annie wrote over 150 authoritative articles and papers on every conceivable aspect of bees and bee-keeping, from anatomy to diseases, from flight to honey and pollen.

Her book 'Practical Bee Anatomy' published in 1922 gave full details of embryology as well as the external and internal structures of bees, and was related at all stages to observed bee behaviour. Her training and experience in aeronautics comes through from time to time, for example, the air flow over a moving body in relation to the pressure reduction at the surface of the main thoracic spiracle, leading to a natural outflow of air in flight. This she linked with the breathlessness of a heavily laden bee on arrival at the hive, caused by slower flight as well as the extra expenditure of muscular energy. As might be expected, she wrote excellent accounts of bee aeronautics, the actual flight of a bee and allied subjects. She calculated that a bee used six to eight times more energy flying than walking.

Full details of microscopic techniques, reagents, embedding, staining, dissection and mounting were also given in this book. In the microscopic detection of nosema spores, she described their size as 4–6 microns, very similar in size to the smallest pollen grain (myosotis or forget-me-not) which was 5 microns long and shaped like a dumb-bell. This gave non-scientific beekeepers an easy aid to their identification.

Her 'Diseases of Bees' 1934 (second edition 1951) gave very clear accounts of signs, causes and treatment. Most are still valid today, but of course, she wrote before the advent of Fumidil B when she said that 'There is no drug which has proved effective against nosema'.

The modern electron microscope has unravelled what were still mysteries in 1950, but her books have so much plainly stated commonsense that they are still worth reading today. She sensibly devoted three pages to 'causes of needless anxiety'.

In her reporting, she criticized unmercifully publications which contained bold assertions of new discoveries supported only by nebulous theories and inaccurate quotations. She fought the battle for exact scientific work, and above all, re-examined problems which had been thought explained and disposed of years ago, correcting many common misunderstandings.

In her own words, 'Research is a hard and long-winded task, governed by a severe discipline'. She also said, 'The busy amateur may do very good work. For that, sharp eyes and accurate note-taking, not a great deal of time, are essential'. About International Conferences she wrote, 'I always think that the most valuable side of such meetings is the chance for private talk with colleagues from other lands. Not just demonstrations or readings of papers, but plenty of time for everyone to sit about and talk'.

Her editorship of 'Bee World' from 1929–1949 covered the difficult war years, during which she sometimes had to write the whole journal herself, which she said she hated doing. During this period she became increasingly deaf and complained of the deadly boredom of not being able to have a conversation. For her last few years she lived an isolated life and communicated only by correspondence.

There is little space to quote extracts from her books, but perhaps her detailed analysis of the colour changes in the eyes and body of a worker pupa may be useful.

Day 13	eyes still white
Day 14	eyes pink
Day 15	eyes lilac
Day 16	eyes purple
Day 17	eyes dark purple
	body yellow
Day 18	body changes from
	yellow to brown
Day 19/20	final moult—
	adult bee
Day 21	young bee emerges

She also mentioned that under warm conditions, e.g. at the centre of a comb, the 21 days could be shortened by 12–18 hours.

Conversely, in colder conditions (at the edge of a comb) lengthened by almost a full day.

A member of the Royal Aeronautical Society for many years, in fact until her death, Annie was actively engaged in basic aeronautical research as early as the First World War. Her paper on empirical formulae for variable pitch airscrews in 1918 involved wind tunnel work as well as flights from Martlesham Heath, using an S.E.5 biplane specially fitted with a Wolseley Viper engine. This work was published under the name of Miss A. D. Betts B.Sc. assisted by H. A. Mettam, as Report No. 577, Tech. Dept. Air Ministry, Feb. 1919.

CHAPTER TWENTY

PROFESSOR KARL R. VON FRISCH 1886–1982

Karl von Frisch wrote his doctoral thesis at the age of twenty-four on colour vision and hearing in fish, and it was not until 1921 that he turned to bees, which then became his great interest for life. He will be remembered chiefly for his classic work on bee language, by which bees communicate information about where to find nectar: how far and on what direction to look for it. In his own words (1953)—'Suppose German and English bees were living together in the same hive, and one of the Germans found a lot of nectar; its English companions would easily understand what it had to say about the distance and direction of the find. Human language is not so perfect. So I am indebted to Dr. Dora Isle for translating my book—"The Dancing Bees"—for English readers.'

In a short article it is impossible to describe all the variations, but briefly, if the nectar source is less than about 80 metres away, the bee dance is a round one carrying just the message 'Lots of food close by: go out and look for it.' For greater distances, the dance is a figure of eight with the straight part making the same angle with the vertical on the comb in the hive, as the flight direction outside must do with the direction of the sun.

Before unravelling the dance language, von Frisch studied colour perception by bees, following his original work on fish. Bees were given a small dish of honey on a table two hundred metres away. It was some time before the first bee noticed it, but soon after that bee flew back to the hive, several others followed, knowing that the first bee had told them where to fly. The next step was to remove the honey pot and replace it with a few drops of honey on blue paper.

After allowing the bees to fly to and fro a few times, he removed the honeyed paper and replaced it with two new papers, one red and one blue, on either side of the original position, but without any honey at all.

The bees flew to and began to land on the blue paper, but showed no interest in the red. They remembered that food had been offered on blue and were able to distinguish between red and blue colours. It would have been premature to conclude from this that bees have colour vision, as some humans who are colour blind can still distinguish between red and blue paper, seeing red as a darker grey than blue. Like the true scientist that he was, von Frisch then used a whole series of grey papers, ranging from pure white to almost black, and placed the clean blue sheet (without food) in among the grey papers. The bees still flew directly towards the blue paper. It worked even better when the grey papers were left on the table all the time, so that the overall pattern was familiar. This clearly showed that bees can distinguish blue as a colour.

By further experiments it was established that bees see four colours: yellow, blue-green, blue and ultra-violet. To them, red is normally seen as black, with the proviso that some colours red to humans contain some mauve. Others, like poppy blossom for example, reflect ultra-violet light and are therefore seen as this colour by bees.

Von Frisch went on to show that bees are able to perceive polarized light, and to use it as a navigational aid. He also demonstrated that bees use the scent of flowers as a guide when close up. This was done by using several identical tiny boxes each with a small hole, on a table which bees had already been trained to visit. Only one of the boxes had scent, whether of actual flowers concealed inside or alternatively, a dab of perfume like Oil of Jasmine; the bees would rapidly find the scented box and enter it. He appreciated that the first bees to enter reinforced the natural scent by the use of their own scent glands (Nassanov).

Among many other detailed discoveries were the following:

1948 – that when the bees have to fly against a head wind, a greater distance is indicated, and vice versa.

1949 – that when bees have to fly around a mountain or other obstacle, the direction given is a straight line to the objective. The bees then apply a correction to get back on course.

1950 – that the sun's position can be used even if the sun be behind cloud, so long as a small patch of blue sky is there. They manage even without this with thin cloud cover.

1951 – that the language of bees does differ, but only slightly, Italian (ligustica) bees having a slower dance rhythm than Austrian (carnica) bees.

Thus it is possible to say that (i) a bee flies to the vicinity of an important nectar source by using the sun as a compass, having been given direction and distance by a dancing scout bee, (ii) the actual area is defined by colour, (iii) the precise source is identified (when very close) by scent. Karl von Frisch even noticed that a small number of eccentric bees ignored scout bees and continued to search for additional nectar sources! As with human society, this underlines the value of a few non-conformists, who do not follow like sheep the accepted philosophy of the day, in whatever field of thought. In respect of '(i)' the sun does not have to be directly visible, but the bees know where it is in a cloudy sky by detecting the plane of polarized light. His work also covered the dances by scout bees on the side of a clustered swarm, and he clearly understood the 'debate' between bees which had discovered alternative sites. Factors such as shelter from prevailing wind, space available in relation to size of swarm, absence of ants (i.e. off the ground). Distance also came into the equation, three hundred yards being preferred to thirty. As a humble student and admirer of Karl von Frisch I have on many occasions spent a happy hour beside a clustered swarm, and noted separate and distinct dances, for example one indicating a site about half a mile to the S.W. and another three hundred yards to the N.E. The more energetic and enthusiastic the dance, the more conviction they carried, until the less popular site almost ceased to have any advocates at all. Some years ago (when I chased swarms more than I do today), I developed a 'rule of thumb', i.e. (a) on finding a clustered swarm, check for indication of a debate, (b) if all dances indicated the same site, take the swarm quickly. On one occasion I remember noting similar dance patterns on a large swarm in a Paignton garden, but on return five minutes later after collecting gear from my car parked some distance away, found the swarm taking off and vanishing into the distance. For a full account of this (and much more), read von Frisch's book 'The Dancing Bees', translated into English in 1953.*

This great man, who by his work so illuminated our knowledge of bee behaviour, served as a professor at three other universities before taking the chair of Zoology at the University of Munich, where he was co-winner of a Nobel Prize for his work. The B.B.K.A. was itself honoured that he accepted Honorary Membership of our national Association.

Martin Lindauer, a student of Professor von Frisch at Munich, worked with him in the later stages of his work and continued after his retirement. In fact Lindauer developed much of von Frisch's earlier work and made interesting discoveries himself. In his own Harvard Lecture (1959) he paid generous tribute to his colleague and former teacher. Lindauer's book 'Communication among Social Bees' (Harvard University Press 1961) should also be read by those wishing to study the topic more deeply.

Diagrams on p. 83 are from 'The Dancing Bees' by Karl von Frisch.

---

* Publisher's note: This book is out of print, but Von Frisch's 'Bees: Their vision, chemical senses and language' 1968 is still available and covers the subject.

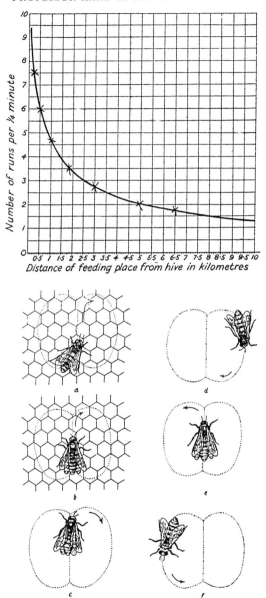

The wagging dance: on vertical combs; nectar source directly towards sun

CHAPTER TWENTY-ONE

R. O. B. MANLEY 1888–1978

Possibly the greatest commercial beekeeper in British history, and as good a writer on bee matters as he was a practical beekeeper, Manley began in 1906, when he first saw supers of honey, white with new wax on a neighbour's fifteen hives, roughly made from Tate & Lyle sugar boxes. He made himself two Cottager hives within a few days, bought in two driven swarms and carried them home on a motor-bike early in August. After hiving them, he fed sugar syrup (they took down a quart a night). Then he bought a complete skep of bees for a golden half sovereign, set it up on a round board on a stake and all three stocks wintered well. In one of his books he recalls the thrills of the following Spring, when he first handled frames of newly-drawn comb and saw eggs and larvae for the first time, also the queen walking among her workers.

Next year (1907) was a terrible season and his total crop was an old wash-stand water jug full of honey, which he sold in Nottingham for 6d (two and a half new pence) a pound. However, he travelled around, driving bees from skeps for cottagers, who would otherwise have killed them with burning sulphur fumes. Here he learned the advantage of large skeps (as used by Pettigrew).

Despite deep snow in April, 1908 was a very good year (he had to buy nine gross of 1 pound jars for £5) as as a novice was examined (for his elementary certificate) by a young man called William Herrod. One practical test was to drive bees from a skep and catch the queen as she came up.

He said at the end of his life that he never knew a better honey year than 1911; the bees were strong in Spring and in June/July the days started with a heavy dew, but in strong sun became 'steamy hot' by 11.00 a.m. and the honey poured in for weeks. Stocks built combs under floors and then outside hives, and some beekeepers took two to three years to sell the huge crops.

This made him think in terms of larger hives, and in 1915, he bought two commercial hives from Simmins (on 16 × 10 inch frames). Then after reading American books, he went one stage further, adopted modified Dadant hives and decided to make his living from honey production. From then on, he castigated orthodox British methods, which he said 'always found some excuse for doing something to the bees', and 'the poor little creatures were tormented from March until winter brought rest'. He made sarcastic remarks about 'photos of smiling old gentlemen fiddling about with complicated hives piled high with supers, all as empty as dummy bottles in a grocer's shop'.

Apiary Sites

Manley felt that about forty stocks per apiary was enough. He did have ninety in one place, but it was an isolated one where few other bees were situated within three miles, and flora were good and abundant. He believed that bees should be so placed that they could collect all the nectar they could carry in their working hours within a radius of about three quarters of a mile (1,300 yards/1,200 m).

Hives

Manley said rudely that white W.B.C.s were for amateurs, and settled for modified Dadant single brood chambers with eleven short-lugged Hofman frames. Outside measurements 20 × 18$\frac{1}{2}$ × 11$\frac{1}{2}$ inches deep. His supers were 6$\frac{1}{4}$ inches deep. He stuck to Dadants and never wished to change, often repeating, 'If I had known of a better hive, I would have used it'. He often criticized the National Hive, with no bee space over the frames. All his super frames had top and bottom bars 1$\frac{1}{8}$ inch wide for rapid and easy uncapping. In his view, queen excluders were an absolute necessity for practical bee farmers, and he preferred the wire type. If he used zinc excluders they had to be short-slotted (for greater strength). He preferred fairly thick wax foundation. On each hive he kept Brother Adam type feeders, bitumen painted inside, 3$\frac{1}{2}$ inches deep and holding two gallons of syrup. Smokers had to be as large as possible, burning rotten hessian sacking; in his day, easily obtained from farm rubbish-dumps.

Bees

On the subject of Old English black bees, he said that those who praised the memory of them would be none too pleased if they had them today; he did agree that they made good sections of honey, used little propolis and little food in winter, living from flow to flow, but they were aggressive, nervous and produced small honey crops. He preferred Italian bees, which were easy to handle and more prolific.

Manley kept his queens for two full seasons only before re-queening, which he did very simply. He would routinely remove an old queen at the end of July or early August, and six days later destroy all queen cells except one or two open ones with a lavish supply of Royal Jelly. After three weeks he would check and almost always find a fine laying queen. He carried out some queen breeding and always kept a breeder queen in use for two years in order to judge her by the work of her daughters. He believed that drones carried the genes responsible for temper, and that young queens normally mated within a short distance from the hive and at no great height; when they returned un-mated, they were usually back in about five minutes. He noted that in good weather, a young queen would be laying about ten to twelve days after emerging from her cell.

In his 'Bee-keeping in Britain' Manley gives details of how he used thymol in autumn-fed syrup to prevent fermentation; bees suffered no ill-effects from it, even with very late feeding and with syrup unsealed in cells. In a separate section on nosema, he just stated that he had no experience of it, so had to refer to the experience of others. By a coincidence, I have had no experience of nosema these last twelve years, since I started to feed thymol routinely in Autumn. I wonder if there is any connection?

His recipe was 1 ounce thymol crystals dissolved in 5 fluid ounces of surgical spirit, to give a stock solution enough to treat half a ton of sugar (made into syrup). I normally use 4 mls (a teaspoonful) per gallon or 5 litre can of syrup containing 8 to 9 pounds of sugar. No great virtue in exact quantities (hives differ in numbers of bees anyway).

He also gave full details of his use of Oil of Wintergreen (methyl salicylate) to control acarine, and said that he had no serious losses from acarine infestation in apiaries so treated. He did mention exceptions, in respect of stocks headed by American queens, and attributed this to lack of resistance on the part of stocks coming from acarine-free areas. Brother Adam has had similar experience when using New Zealand queens.

Manley used a 1 ounce bottle with a wick standing on the floor in one corner, renewed annually, and said that it seemed to prevent the mites from migrating, i.e. they avoided exposure to the fumes by staying in the trachea—so no spread of the trouble. I have used small ex-shoe polish tins stuffed with wadding, and about 6–8 small holes in lid (by a hammered nail). Just a thought—but one wonders if varroa mites might also be discouraged by this substance. Varroa did not exist in Manley's time, of course.

His first book 'Honey Production in the British Isles' (1936) rapidly sold out and needed a second edition. 'Honey Farming' followed in 1946 and in 1948 came his third and last book, 'Beekeeping in Britain', which not only summarizes a lifetime of making a living from bees, but was also a full treatment of the whole subject. He conjured up memories of beekeeping in the nineteen thirties, those warm, sultry days in the Chiltern Hills; the magnificent white clover flowers, the hum of worker bees among the blossoms of meadow and hedgerow.

In the last ten to twelve years of his life, he suffered from the effects of one or two strokes; this and his acute deafness made him avoid the company of others, but many sought his advice. His books are still highly regarded.

CHAPTER TWENTY-TWO

EDMOND ALPHANDÉRY 1870–1941: RAOUL ALPHANDÉRY 1901–1990

Many have followed their fathers as beekeepers but seldom has the son achieved fame to equal that of a great father. Probably the best example of this can be found in a close look at the life and work of these two great Frenchmen, who between them edited and produced the magazine 'a Gazette Apicole' for over eighty years. Descended from the famous doctor Mosse Alphandéry, who in 1518 was called by the Pope to treat victims of the plague in Avignon, Edmond's father was Aristippe Alphandéry, the great agronomist and chemist of the 19th century, known especially for his work on soils and flora. When on military service with an artillery regiment in Nîmes at the age of twenty, he first read about bees and made up his mind to devote his life to them. As soon as his military training had finished he began to keep bees and continued throughout his life. In his own words, 'Since the day I first read "Managing an Apiary" by Edward Bertrand, I was transported a hundred leagues from the 38th Regiment of Artillery to gardens of flowers, green meadows, fields of lavender and herbs, and decided that the only possible profession for me was beekeeping.'

At the age of thirty Edmond founded that great bee journal '*La Gazette Apicole*', which he continued to edit for the next forty years.

He wrote twelve bee books and finally in 1931 produced his '*Traité Complet d'Apiculture*', which ran to 571 large pages 11 × 8·6 inches (280 × 220 mm), equivalent to well over 1,000 pages of a normal book, with over 900 illustrations. This was (and remains) an encyclopaedia of beekeeping, comparable to the much better known American 'ABC and XYZ of Bee-keeping', but apparently has never been translated into English.

So far as I know, there are no specific items of equipment or beekeeping techniques linked to his name, but on studying his writings, one is impressed by the evidence of a keen mind and lively intelligence backed by vast experience. His major book covers every possible aspect of the craft, from prehistoric times via the Egyptians, to classical Greece and the present day. On bees themselves he analyses the evidence as to whether they are intelligent beings or activated only by instinct.

His conclusion was that they show intelligence in many examples where they modify their activities to adapt to different circumstances.

Edmond made a detailed study of yields from comparable hives with a natural complement of drones, as opposed to hives where

drones had been suppressed or eliminated. Despite the high con-
sumption of honey involved in the production and maintenance of
the males, it became clear that colonies worked better and stored
more honey with them than without them. Many experienced
beekeepers today have confirmed that this is so. Possibly a yet
undiscovered pheromone produced by drones is responsible for this.
He also analysed factors involved in choosing apiary sites, and
whether bees did better in bee houses or in the open. He found in
favour of open air, but this conclusion would not necessarily be
valid in the more continental climate of Germany and Central
Europe.

Every aspect of the craft was most thoroughly covered, from the
earliest records to modern practice, with full notes on beeswax,
mead, pollen, comb and liquid honey, even vinegar production. He
gave credit to the sloping sides of the Greek basket hives, which
enabled combs hanging from single top-bars to be lifted out for
inspection or making artificial swarms. Strangely this principle was
never adopted elsewhere and for centuries before Langstroth (1851)
the nuisance of combs fastened to vertical hive sides was accepted.
The pipe hives of Egypt might perhaps be regarded as depending
on the same principle, but without the advantages of comb lifting
and replacing.

Raoul Alphandéry

The son of Edmond was brought up among bees from babyhood
and took his first swarm at the age of $6\frac{1}{2}$ years. In later years he was
a well-known figure at International Bee Conferences and became a
close friend of William Herrod-Hempsall and more recently Cecil
Tonsley. Apart from his beekeeping activities he was an adviser to
the French Government on foreign trade and was rewarded by
appointment as a Knight of the Legion of Honour.

Exactly twelve years after his father's great book, he produced his
book 'Un Rucher Nait' (1943) which ran to five editions and over
50,000 copies. Arranged in forty chapters, each being a full lesson
in a progressive study of beekeeping with magnificent colour photographs, I know of no English equivalent. Each one of these chapters
condenses the background and knowledge involved into just three

to five well-illustrated pages, capable of being separately read and studied. One exception is Chapter 17 which devotes six pages to the queen (1981 edtn.).

Sub-titled '40 Leçons d'apiculture' this book would be a great help to any beekeeper studying at home and perhaps unable to attend lectures on aspects covered. Alas, it is only available in French.

On the death of his father, Raoul took over as Editor of 'La Gazette Apicole' and continued for another forty years.

CHAPTER TWENTY-THREE

DOROTHY HODGES
1898–1979

The main contribution of this beekeeper was her work on pollen and its collection by honey-bees. She will be remembered with affection as the author and illustrator of 'The Pollen Loads of Honey-bees', which has given pleasure to so many. Trained as an artist, she started her beekeeping only in May 1940 with a four-frame nucleus, never having seen bees handled before, and spent much time just sitting by her hive and watching the bees. Then she began drawing and painting bees, especially those carrying pollen, and so began her lifelong interest in pollen loads and their identification.

Colour Charts

She described to me many years ago how she used to hunt for a bee with large pollen loads, busy on a flower; she would creep up close with a small gauze cage in one hand and a lid in the other, drop the cage on top and slip the lid underneath, sometimes catching a bit of the flower also. Petrol was rationed then, and when there was none, she used a bicycle. If not too far away, she would cycle home, release the bee on to a window, then pick her up by the wings and gently push off the pollen loads before setting her free. Then she would match the exact colour (using Winsor and Newton watercolours) and record the name of the flower, before mounting the pollen specimen as a permanent record. It was amusing to hear her describe her embarrassment when she saw a bee, working on an unusual plant, inside someone's front garden. Should she ring the bell to ask permission, and risk that the bee would have flown away, or take a chance and just go ahead, trusting that no-one would notice? She feared that any passers-by must sometimes have thought her quite dotty, so she would hastily hide her equipment and stroll away, pretending that all was normal.

Her First Microscope

Dr Colin Butler, then Head of the Bee Department at Rothamsted, asked her to make drawings of pollen grains, for reference by researchers who were trapping pollen in hives, and sorting specimens by colour, for identification under a microscope. So, as she modestly said, a whole new world was revealed, with all the varied and exquisite details of different pollen grains. Her drawings of them as seen under a microscope are much better than optical micro-photographs, as the drawn detail is uniformly sharp, being a sum-mation of what is seen by the artist in focusing up.

The camera records just that part actually in focus at the moment of the exposure, and keen photographers will appreciate the limi-tations of 'field of focus' involved with ultra close-up work on microscopic objects.

Towards the end of her book are thirty full page plates of nearly two hundred individual pollen grains, carefully drawn to scale. They range from the giant vegetable marrow and hollyhock (diameters 140–150 microns) to the forget-me-not (diameter 5 microns).

In conversation with some non-beekeepers, I have realized that 'pollen loads' are sometimes thought of as if they are 'pollen grains'. In fact, of course, the average 'pollen load' of apple or clover pollen (each individual grain of diameter of about 25 microns), weighing

20 to 30 mg, would contain well over 100,000 grains themselves, like flour. (One inch = 25,000 microns).

The Book

When, after several years this work was nearly complete, it was suggested that it be published in book form. 'The Pollen Loads of the Honey Bee' was in fact published in 1952 by the Bee Research Association (now prefixed by 'International'), after many difficulties had been overcome. At the end of her book are six full colour pages of 120 different pollen colours, almost all of these including three hand-painted squares to indicate possible variations of colour to be found in practice. Each of the 350 paper slips was cut from large sheets of hand-painted colour, giving 14 mm squares which were individually pasted in.

The pollens are carefully arranged in sequence according to normal dates of flowering, from laurestinus (*viburnum tinis*) and winter heather (*erica carnea*) in early spring to common ivy (*hedera helix*) in late October.

To protect these water-colour paintings, the plates are interleaved with tissue, and should not be left open for long periods in a strong light.

First Blossoms—Survey

Year	Plum (Early Rivers)	Apple (Beauty of Bath)	Horse Chestnut
1942	25 April	1 May	24 May
1943	3 April	15 April	8 May
1944	12 April	27 April	11 May
1945	1 April	12 April	18 April
1946	3 April	16 April	30 April
1947	24 April	6 May	8 May
1948	23 March	12 April	22 April
1949	5 April	16 April	26 April
1950	16 March	22 April	9 May
1951	20 April	9 May	16 May

I must confess to having had a page open at a hive side to enjoy for example, the pleasure of a bee carrying a load of brick-red chestnut pollen, walking over pollen slip No. 48 (late spring to early summer). She also made some exquisite drawings, of which the old English Wicker Hive, drawn from a small picture in a 14th century psalm book, is an example.

Fourteenth-century wicker hive drawn by Dorothy Hodges and published with acknowledgement to Mrs Hodges and to the Trustees of the British Museum.

I was privileged to enjoy the friendship of Dorothy and Jack Hodges on returning to England in 1964, and when advancing years and ill-health took their toll, she passed on to me the microscope with which she had worked. She presented her original slides to the Bee Research Association (then at Hill House, Bucks) and had put out some well-used empty slide cabinets for the dustman, but at the last moment brought them inside and got Jack to post them to me! Finally, after a long illness and periods of treatment in Epsom Hospital, she joined other Bee Masters in the Heavenly Gardens.

CHAPTER TWENTY-FOUR

COLIN G. BUTLER O.B.E., F.R.S. 1913–

After gaining a First Class (Natural Science Tripos II) at Cambridge, Butler studied whiteflies under a Ministry of Agriculture scholarship, and became Superintendent of the Cambridge University Entomological Field Station (1937–1939); here he also carried out research on the physiology of locusts before taking charge of the bee section of Rothamsted Entomological Department. Under his able leadership, in 1944 the Bee Section became an independent department, and some years later Butler was promoted to lead the whole Department of Entomology.

The influence of the queen on a colony of bees interested Butler from his earliest days at Rothamsted and by 1952 he was convinced that the source of this influence was a 'queen substance' secreted by the queen and circulated throughout the colony workers. By a series of controlled experiments he discovered that 'queen substance' contained a pheromone which inhibited the rearing of additional queens. During the next twenty years he made a detailed study of the interaction of queens and bee colonies and presented fifteen or more scientific papers on various aspects of this. These were published in a range of scientific periodicals from the prestigious 'Nature' to the 'Journal of Entomology'. His great achievement was the identification of different queen pheromones and their functions, individually and collectively. In this work he was greatly assisted by regular supplies of queens from Brother Adam at Buckfast, after they had been removed from working hives and replaced. This enabled him to prepare, for example, extracts from queens' mandibular glands and use in some of his experiments.

In 1972 I was privileged to attend the annual week at Rothamsted with about two dozen county bee instructors and enjoyed hearing from Butler himself some of the fascinating details. I remember being one of a small group in his study discussing the mating flight of a queen, and the almost unbelievable persistence of the queen substance extracted from their mandibular glands. Keen on sailing, Butler described how he had used such an extract smeared on the tip of a tall aluminium mast (from his boat). After nine years this mast still attracted drones when he went sailing in August on the River Ouse, although stored in the open air for years!

I also remember a vigorous debate in class when Ken Stevens (Kent) and I took issue with the use of the terms 'up-wind' and 'down-wind' in the context of queen and drones flying freely in moving air; it proved quite difficult to explain the point, even to such a distinguished group of land-lubbers.

Butler's first book 'An Introduction to Beekeeping' was published in 1948, followed a year later by M.A.F. Bulletin No. 144 'Beehives' (H.M.S.O.) and 'The Honeybee. An Introduction to her Sense-physiology and Behaviour' (Oxford, Clarendon Press) 1949. His best-known book is certainly 'The World of the Honeybee' published by Collins in the New Naturalist Series in 1954. This is a classic for all time, most strongly recommended to beekeepers, and to anyone else interested in bees and their ways. A revised Bulletin No. 9 of the official M.A.F. 'Beekeeping' by Colin Butler was published by H.M.S.O. in 1945, 1946, 1951 and 1957.*

Butler will always be associated with and remembered by his work

* Publisher's Note. The last edition of this useful booklet was in October 1981.

on queen pheromones, on which he became the world authority and for which he received the coveted Fellowship of the Royal Society, founded three hundred years earlier by a small group led by another great beekeeper, the Rev. John Wilkins*.

CHAPTER TWENTY-FIVE

NORMAN V. RICE M.B.E.
1922–

Norman Rice of Australia will be remembered by many people in many different ways, but perhaps most vividly by Third World beekeepers for his help over so many years, at all levels, not just with paperwork in the offices of government ministries, but mainly at the ground roots of beekeeping, with hands in hives many miles from officialdom, sharing the sweat and dust, the discomfort and sheer hard work. All this, year after year, from China to Pakistan, from Iran to Indonesia, not as a casual visitor, but at the repeated requests of the governments concerned.

By his life, he has also demonstrated that a man can rise to the top by his own efforts, without formal education, training or backing from anyone (except his wife, Heather!) More than this, having reached the top he kept that 'common touch', equally at home with world authorities like Woyke, Ruttner, Maul, Tilly Khunant *et al*, but also with humble beekeepers like Mr Lung from Hong Kong, the sons of North American commercial beekeepers, sent to him to gain experience, and so on. All these and many more have enjoyed the hospitality of Norman and Heather in Queensland.

* Publisher's Note. Butler also wrote with John Free 'Bumblebees' in the Collins New Naturalist series, 1959 which is much sought after and is a scarce book today. (See half-tone section for a photograph of them both).

Norman's first encounter with bees was as a schoolboy at a one-teacher school in a remote farming area of Queensland, where he and his four younger brothers and sisters made up a third of the school roll, travelling to and fro on horseback. His interest was kindled by a school visit by a local beekeeper with a swarm; by a coincidence, a day or two later he saw a similar swarm on a bush beside the rough track on the way home. He took it in the empty family lunch box, a leather back-pack, rode home with it and hived it in an empty butter box; alas, the swarm decamped next day, leaving two small combs. Lesson One—that bees have to be protected from the hot sun of Northern Australia.

After his parents moved to Brisbane his next colony survived in the back yard for a year, but like Herrod-Hempsall at the same age, he opened them up too often and they never really developed.

As a youth of sixteen, working away from home with the Forestry Department, he became expert in taking wild bee colonies from trees. Then came the Second World War and six years' very active service with the Royal Australian Navy, most of the time afloat in the mine-sweeper H.M.A.S. 'Ararat'.

Demobilized, his small ex-service grant bought a taxi and long hours driving, to support wife Heather and a growing family. His next hive of bees soon multiplied into forty, then two hundred, and before long, bees took over his life and he became a full-time commercial beekeeper. Raising queen bees began in a small way, about six per week, but in a few years, to over 30,000 a year, sent around the entire world.

World Problems

Like organizing bees with a management system to fit the seasonal demand in the varying climatic patterns of the entire world and dove-tailing this into a human social pattern where employed staff work only a five-day week and bees for seven days. Like working with complex air-freight schedules linking Brisbane with the rest of the world, subject to seasonal holidays and strikes. Like ensuring that enough queens are on hand to meet a sudden order for three hundred from Pakistan for instant delivery. Like planning the packaging so that bees may survive transhipment at other airports, by staff ignorant of their needs. In short, to go where no man had gone before.

To illustrate just one of the problems a world-supplier of queens and nuclei has to face: the demand in the Northern Hemisphere (Europe, North America, Russia, etc.) is for queens in March/April/May, involving a build-up starting in January. The demand in the Southern Hemisphere and most of the tropics is for queens in October/November/December, needing a production line start-up in August. So only June and July for holidays and maintenance work (plus slightly less work in January and August, perhaps).

Breeder Queen Management

There are many aspects of queen rearing which could be quoted, but just one will have to suffice. Having tried many methods, Norman finally settled years ago for half-size Langstroth boxes, capable of holding either six full depth frames lengthwise or twelve full depth half frames crosswise. One half of the box is divided into two 3-frame compartments by the insertion of two queen excluder slides, when the other half holds five frames. The queen is confined on Day One to the central compartment, and to begin with, frames 4 and 6 contain mostly young larvae, usually with some honey above; the central frame 5 should be a good, dark, brood comb into which the queen is to lay. Frames 7 to 11 should hold emerging brood, honey and pollen; over the next three days, frames 7, 8 and 9 will be successively removed to hold frames of eggs from the central compartment.

On Day Two, frame 7 is removed and replaced with the frame of eggs from position 5, into which a fresh empty brood comb must go.
On Day Three, frame 8 is removed, the new frame 7 moved into its place, and yet another fresh brood comb put in position 5, to be filled with eggs.
On Day Four, the progression is continued with frame 9 being removed; frames 7 and 8 are moved forward and the third frame of eggs from position 5 is inserted in position 7 to fill

the space. From now on, larvae to graft into queen cups are available daily; they are all about twelve hours old, plus or minus six hours.

All that is necessary from here on is to keep replacing frame 5 each day and moving frames forward as before. The colony needs to be supported by frames of sealed or hatching brood from other support colonies maintained for that purpose. If grafting only once a week, then it is only necessary to place an empty comb in space 5 four days before the larvae are needed for grafting. When the brood emerges from frames 4 and 6, these should be replaced, otherwise the queen might lay there.

If the queen is no longer being used to produce larvae for grafting, the two queen-excluder slides should be removed and a full-length queen-excluder plus honey super added over the brood box.

Warming Honey

Even in sub-tropical Brisbane/Beaudesert, about the same distance from the Equator as the Canary Isles, there are advantages most of the year in warming honey supers before extraction. Norman showed the way here, by designing and building his own 'hot room' 16 × 12 feet (4.8 × 3.6 m), floor-heated and well-insulated.

Copper pipes $\frac{5}{8}$ inch (16 mm) spaced 8 inches (20 cm) apart, wrapped in thick brown paper (ex sugar bags) were set in a 4 inch (10 cm) concrete floor. A small pump circulated the hot water from a tank heated by cheap off-peak electricity. No forced air circulation, upward convection currents did this. Capable of holding over four hundred supers (Langstroths), which often only needed to be warmed up 10°F, the extra honey extracted more than paid the electricity bill; faster and easier uncapping was a bonus.

Trapping Pollen

In Australia (as in parts of the U.S.A. and elsewhere) there are periods of the year when shortage of protein from natural pollen is a limiting factor. Commercial beekeepers then have to move colonies off a nectar flow to allow bees to work a good protein source before returning them, otherwise bee populations decline rapidly. In his book 'Queens' Land' Norman illustrates this point by quoting the occasion when a Queensland beekeeper came out of hospital to find not a single living bee in a yard of ninety hives, despite an average of 100 pounds (45 kg) of capped honey on each. The old field bees had worked themselves to death and through lack of pollen, no new bees had been produced. Australian experience has shown that even a minor lack of body protein results in a shorter life for worker bees, and that an *abundant source of pollen* is *an essential factor* in the *production of first-class queens*. Over many years, Norman tried every kind of available pollen substitute, even imported micro-algae, but found nothing to equal natural pollen. So at first, special bee yards were set up to trap pollen when it was plentiful; this was stored in large deep freezers and later fed to colonies producing queen cells.

Subsequently, Norman improved on this by devising and perfecting his own pollen trap, using a plastic sheet with holes punched to allow worker bees to pass through. This removed pollen from the pollen baskets of bees returning to the hive, but because it was plastic, did not damage the bees, as some existing traps (with metal grids) had been found to do. After further trials, the final version had a device to allow the bees to bypass the grid when pollen was no longer plentiful. Also this was to be made an integral part of hive floors, so as to allow hives so fitted to be loaded onto trucks by a boom loader. The pollen being trapped was collected in a drawer having half the width of the hive, and could be harvested without any disturbance to the colony. Indeed, it had to be, every three to five days or in the warm and humid hive atmosphere, raw pollen would rapidly grow a mould. When bees store pollen in cells themselves, they add honey and possibly other substances to preserve it.

'Queens' Land'

His book covers every detail of management and equipment needed for the production of thousands of queens a month, including wax cell cup production, the feeding of bees for queen cell production, the production of frames of larvae for grafting, the setting up of mating yards, the distribution of queen cells and the catching of queens. Problems associated with filling cages with escorts of worker bees at the rate of six hundred per hour and then running in the queens, are also covered. The system outlined can be adapted to more modest needs, whether of fewer larvae grafted at a time, or once a week instead of daily.

Half-size Langstroth brood boxes similar to those used for the production of larvae are also used for queen mating, with three metal slides separating four compartments, each with their own entrance.

The production of package bees, also of 5-frame nuclei (as air-freighted to Kuwait regularly) are fully described.

The commercial production of sixty to seventy tons of honey a year as a by-product serves to underline the scale of his business. His book covers every aspect of the large-scale production and sale of pollen and of honey, the feeding of colonies with sugar syrup. Artificial insemination is also covered, as is the marking of queens. (Diagram of half-Langstroth broodbox)

At a personal level, Norman describes the development of his beekeeping career, with the mistakes made on the way and how these were rectified. In this book are innumerable tips on practical points dealing with every aspect of beekeeping.

CHAPTER TWENTY-SIX

REV. BROTHER ADAM O.B.E. 1898–

Born in South Germany, Karl Kerle came to Buckfastleigh in March 1910, as a pupil renamed Louis to be educated by the monks of Buckfast, with the possibility of being selected for the priesthood or to follow one of the crafts necessary for the rebuilding and main-tenance of the Abbey.

Louis did well at school, and renamed Adam, was accepted as a novice in 1914 and also put to assist the stonemason in the hard work of cutting and dressing the blocks of Bath stone for the Abbey. However, he was not physically strong enough for this job and in March 1915 was made an assistant to Brother Columban, then in charge of bees (about forty-five hives) and the kitchens. In September 1919 Brother Adam took over the bees and remained in charge for over seventy years. As historical background, it should perhaps be stated that although the present Abbey is comparatively new, having been built between 1906 and 1939 by a devoted community of Benedictine monks, it stands on the site of a much older foundation, dissolved by Henry VIII in 1539.

Before the Reformation, bees were kept in skeps by the monks, as by many local people. Bee boles can still be seen in an ancient enclosure wall, across the road from the present Abbey, but there is no record of any special reputation for beekeeping at that time. In 1882, monks returned to Buckfast and once again kept bees in skeps, and in 1895 Brother Columban took over the apiary, introducing some Italian and Carniolan queens, but for the most part the bees were still the old English blacks.

A hint of the fame which history had in store was the record crop of 160 pounds of honey obtained in 1906 by the headmaster of a local school, using a Carniolan queen given to him by Brother Columban. This was remembered and talked about for years in and around Buckfastleigh. About this time, Isle of Wight disease was spreading across England, and the Buckfast bees suffered with the rest. The English Black Bees were virtually wiped out, and by 1915 only sixteen of the Abbey stocks survived. It was noted that all were of Carniolan or Italian origin, so in May 1916 thirty queens were imported (from Piana, Italy) and used to requeen the stocks, split to make up forty-five hives. These built up well and produced an average of 110 pounds a hive that summer. By 1918 the total stocks had risen to one hundred.

Choice of Hive

At first Buckfast had hives of different types but mostly double-walled Burgess Perfection with British Standard frames.

Adam felt that ten British Standard frames in a single brood box gave too little room for the prolific Ligurian queens imported from Italy, so in 1920 first tried out colonies with a double brood box. Results were encouraging. In 1923 he first tried six Modified Dadant hives (twelve frames) and in the next five years made comparative trials with sixty double brood chamber Nationals and sixty M.D. hives, equal numbers in each of three different apiaries. He obtained better results from the larger Dadant hives with a single brood box and by 1930 had completed the changeover to this pattern. Frame spacing was effected by hob-nails, commonly used on working boots at that time but more recently replaced by identical plastic studs. Of course, year by year comparisons are made difficult by abnormal years, such as 1921. In conversation with Brother Adam in 1988 about this particular year, he volunteered the information that he, too, remembered it very well, and that they took nine tons of honey from their sixty hives, the highest crop ever. This, despite the fact that it was too dry for the heather to yield at all.

All his Modified Dadant hives have a bottom bee space, and when I asked why he had chosen this, he replied that he found it better for the bees when moving over the rough ground on Dartmoor. Also, when putting down a super or brood box the bees were less likely to be crushed. Factors against double brood chamber management were the extra labour involved and also the space between the boxes, found by him to restrict the expansion of the brood area by acting as a barrier.

Bee Breeding

Mention has already been made of the use made of exceptional stocks in 1917, headed by cross-bred Italian queens. This was really the beginning of purposeful queen breeding at Buckfast, and in 1920 the field was widened by the importation of Carniolan queens from Yugoslavia, also of Cyprian and Swiss Black Queens. Another milestone was the establishment in June 1925 of a queen mating station at Hexworthy, an isolated spot on Dartmoor, now approaching its seventieth anniversary.

Lesser men than Brother Adam would have been well satisfied by a reputation already firmly established, but the best was yet to come. In the Spring of 1950 was begun the first of those epic journeys so faithfully recorded in his own account 'In Search of the Best Strains of Bees', when he visited Provence in the South of France and Switzerland. The reader is referred to this book for a full record of travels which took Brother Adam from Morocco to Egypt, from Turkey to Greece and the Iberian Peninsula and many other places in twelve busy years. Different though the purpose may have been, to the writer these travels have almost the sublimity and dedication of St Paul's Missionary journeys. The flowering of a genius can only be recognized when time gives us the advantage of hindsight. Brother Adam appreciated at an early stage the supreme importance of the bee itself, as opposed to the secondary matters of hive design, management and machinery. His experience during the years when Isle of Wight disease was taking its toll convinced him that hereditary resistance is much more important than medicine. He appreciated many years ago the weaknesses of line breeding with consequent loss of vigour as well as the genetic limitations necessarily imposed. His experience of queens imported through normal trade channels gave glimpses of the possibilities of cross-breeding, and impelled him to seek personally, on the spot in a number of countries, the best possible strains from which to select queens with genetic characteristics so linked as to be of use in positive breeding programmes.

At a time when widespread hybridization threatens the purity of many types of bees, the samples (of one hundred bees preserved *in vitro*) collected on behalf of Rothamsted Experimental Station from all over Europe and North Africa, constitute a little-known but scientifically most valuable reference datum.

The fruits of this great work have been with us for some years, on an increasing scale. In 1965 Buckfast breeder queens were first supplied to Israel, where better weather conditions allow more reliable mating. There is a story (with no official foundation!) that several batches of Buckfast Queens, ex-Israel, produced colonies of unusual bad temper, and this was ascribed to the siting of mating stations too close to the Syrian border, so that these queens had mismated with Syrian drones. Subsequently breeder queens were sent to Texas and their progeny sold well on the U.S. market as

well as here at home, in Europe, and above all in Sweden. More
recent developments made use of artificial insemination, for which
ampoules of semen from Devon Buckfast drones, together with
combs of eggs from breeder queens were flown by jet across the
Atlantic.

Bee Equipment

Earlier in this article it was stated that Brother Adam recognized
the paramount importance of the bee, as opposed to the design of
the hive, the use of machinery, or management. This has not
precluded a degree of mechanization and standardization at Buckfast
which has had the admiration of professional beekeepers for a great
many years. Modern and gleaming as the workrooms are, with
shining presses, thermostatically controlled mechanical uncappers,
vast, steam-heated storage tanks to carry honey surplus from good
year to bad year, when seeing all this today, it is hard to believe that
all this ultra modern equipment was in place and being used over
sixty years ago; only the absence of stainless steel reveals its age.

When one appreciates that all this was designed by, and much of
it hand-made by Brother Adam himself, working incredibly long
hours and with a minimum of rest and sleep, one senses the quality
of a genius. It has been said that genius needs both inspiration and
perspiration. Here they both are, in good measure.

Not surprisingly, he suffered a break-down in health early in 1932
and spent three months at home in Germany to recuperate. After
more years of superhuman work, he fell ill again in 1939 and had
to spend over three months in sick-bed, his doctor saying that he
had a heart disorder caused by overwork and would never work
again. Ironically, over fifty years later, his doctors (and friends) have
once again been advising him to work less and rest more!

General Points

Some mention must be made of Adam's mead, carefully made by
slow fermentation and even longer maturation in oak casks.

On slow climatic changes, Brother Adam believes that there has,
over the years, been a shift to more dry, cold weather in May and
early June, with the rain coming later, so that prospects on the

Moor have deteriorated. Before 1970 there was only one year (1924) when he did not move bees to the heather; it was so wet this year. Since 1970 there have been at least twelve years when hives have not been taken to Dartmoor in August, as there seemed no hope of a crop.

When asked (in 1988) how he saw the future of beekeeping at Buckfast over the next ten to twenty years, Brother Adam replied that he did not expect anyone to carry on exactly as he had done, but pointed out that there was no building or construction work to be done; anybody should be able to carry on. 'The secret is to note outstanding colonies for choice of line breeding and then cross them to get hybrid vigour. Mr Donovan has done this successfully when I have been away,' said Brother Adam.

It is not possible to say all that could be said in a short article, and the reader is referred to Brother Adam's own books* and also to Lesley Bill's biography 'For the Love of Bees—The Story of Brother Adam of Buckfast Abbey'.

* These are (in English):—
'Beekeeping at Buckfast Abbey' 1st edtn 1975, 4th edtn (with meadmaking) 1987
'In Search of the Best Strain of Bees' 1983
'Breeding the Honeybee' 1987

BIBLIOGRAPHY

Note: A great deal of the material in the book came from many sources other than published books, but this list covers the major published works by the Great Masters.

Abbot, C. N. The British Bee Journal (Bound vols. from May, 1873), London, 1875

Adam, Rev. Brother Beekeeping at Buckfast Abbey, Geddington, 1975

Alphandery, E. Traité Complet d'Apiculture, Paris, 1931

Betts, A. D. Miss Diseases of Bees, Camberley, 1934

Bevan, Dr E. The Honey-bee, London, 1838

Bill, Lesley For the Love of Bees (Biography of Brother Adam), Newton Abbot, 1989

Butler, Rev. C. Feminine Monarchie, Oxford, 1609

Butler, Colin F.R.S. The World of the Honeybee, London, 1954

Cowan, T. W. British Bee-keeper's Guide Book, London, 1881

Devon BKA A thousand years of Devon Beekeeping, Torquay, 1975

Digges, Rev. J. G. Practical Bee Guide, London, Dublin, Belfast, 1928

Dzierzon, Dr J. Rational Bee-keeping (ed. Abbott, C. N.), London, 1882

Evelyn, John F.R.S. Memoirs and Diary, 1819

Frisch, K. von Prof. The Dancing Bees, London, 1954

Hempsall-Herrod, W. Beekeeping New & Old with Pen & Camera, 2 vols, London 1930, 1937

Hodges, D. The Pollen Loads of the Honeybee, London, 1952

Huber, F. Nouvelles Observations sur les Abeilles, Paris, 1814

Isaac, Rev. J. The General Apiarian, Exeter, 1803

Western Apiary Society Transactions, Exeter, 1809

Janscha, A. Handling Bee Swarms, London, 1717

Langstroth, L. L. Rev. The Hive and the Honeybee, New York, 1890

Manley, R. O. B. Bee-keeping in Britain, London, 1948

Neighbour, A. The Apiary, London, 1865

Pepys, S. Diary, London, 1896

Plot, Dr. Robert Natural history of Oxfordshire, London, 1677

Rice, Norman V. Queens' Land (Foreword by Ron Brown), Mytholmroyd, 1946

Snelgrove, L. E. Queen Rearing, Bladon, 1946

Wildman, Thomas A Treatise on the Management of Bees, London, 1768

Index

Advice, to beekeepers 16
Anaesthetics for bees 22
Apiarian societies 32
Apiary sites 12, 41, 85
Apis Club 76
Appliance maker, first 32
Artificial insemination 105

Bee books, most popular 64, 68, 71, 74
Bee books, French 88, 89
Bee boles 102
Beekeepers, in Britain 66
Beekeepers' societies, the first 32
Bees, general description of 13, 79
Bees, introduction to Australia 54
Bee space, discovery 45
Bees, various races 50, 54, 85
Bee World 76
Benzaldehyde, clearing bees 60
Black bees 50, 54
Blossom dates 92
British Bee Journal, foundation 56
Brood boxes 42, 46, 47
Buckfast Abbey 102

Cage, queen introduction 53
Carbolic, use of 65
Chalk brood 76
Colour, perception by bees 21, 80
Comb honey production 43
Comb starters 42
Crystal Palace, honey show 61, 66

Damp hives 50
Dancing bees 14, 79, 83
Devon County Show 70
Driving bees 14
Drones, description of 13
Drones, effect on honey production 89

Escape, bee 60
Excluder, queen 59

Foundation, wax 57
Frame, British standard 56, 66
Frames, moveable 46, 47, 48

Grafting, young larvae 98, 99

Hives, leaf 36, 39
Hives, Dadant 47, 85, 103
Hives, sloping side 89
Hives, W.B.C. 62
Hives, Woodbury 52, 55
Honey extractor 58
Honey, good years 14, 33, 84, 103
Honey shows 72
Honey warming, before extraction 99
House, for bees 22, 28
Hybrid vigour 106

Irish Bee Journal 67
Isle of Wight disease 102

Journal, British Bee 56

King Charles II, bees 18

Langstroth hive 44, 46, 47, 48
Laying workers 36
Leaf hive 36, 39
Lecturer, first beekeeping 24, 25
Liguarian queens 53
Line breeding 104
Management system, 29, 30, 42, 50, 73, 85
Mandibular glands, of queens 95
Mead 31, 35, 105
Metal spacers 62, 65
Moreton hive 34
Moving bees 33